Neural Network Computing

Other books by Ramachandran Bharath
PROLOG: Sophisticated Applications in Artificial Intelligence

Neural Network Computing

Ramachandran Bharath
James Drosen

Windcrest® / McGraw-Hill

New York   San Francisco   Washington, D.C.   Auckland   Bogotá
Caracas   Lisbon   London   Madrid   Mexico City   Milan
Montreal   New Delhi   San Juan   Singapore
Sydney   Tokyo   Toronto

Product or brand names used in this book may be trade names or trademarks. Where we believe that there may be proprietary claims to such trade names or trademarks, the name has been used with an initial capital or it has been capitalized in the style used by the name claimant. Regardless of the capitalization used, all such names have been used in an editorial manner without any intent to convey endoresement of or other affiliation with the name claimant. neither the author nor the publisher intends to express any judgment as to the validity or legal status of any such proprietary cliams.

© 1994 by **Windcrest**.
Published by Windcrest, an imprint of McGraw-Hill, Inc.
The name "Windcrest" is a registered trademark of McGraw-Hill, Inc.

pbk 1 2 3 4 5 6 7 8 9 DOH / DOH 9 9 8 7 6 5 4

Library of Congress Cataloging-in-Publication Data
Bharath, Ramachandran.
    Neural network computing / by Ramachandran Bharath and James
Drosen.
       p.   cm.
    Includes index.
    ISBN 0-8306-4523-3 (pbk.)
    1. Neural networks (Computer science)   I. Drosen, James.
    II. Title.
    QA76.87.B53   1994
    006.3—dc20   94-1199
                                                     CIP

Acquisitions editor: Roland S. Phelps
Editorial team: Bob Ostrander, Executive Editor
                Sally Anne Glover, Book Editor
Production team: Katherine G. Brown, Director
                 Ollie Harmon, Coding
                 Susan E. Hansford, Coding
                 Brenda M. Plasterer, Desktop Operator
                 Cindi Bell, Proofreading
                 Jodi L. Tyler, Indexer
Design team: Jaclyn J. Boone, Designer
             Brian Allison, Associate Designer
Cover design: Margaret Karczewski, Vienna, Va. Marble paper
background by Douglas M. Parks, Blue Ridge Summit, Pa.   WK2
Cover copy writer: Michael Crowner   0051453

R.B. dedicates this book to Mitram and Suchismita. I am using these Sanskrit words for "friend" and "person with an enchanting smile" to refer not to individuals but to the fuzzy sets of all the people who have been important to me at various stages in my life.

J.W.D. dedicates this book to his wife Claudia for her endless support and to R.B. for all his gentle nudging over the years.

Contents

Part 2
Program listings

x

Preface

In the last few years, the subject of artificial neural networks or neural computing has generated a lot of interest and received a lot of coverage in magazines. Naturally, such articles can provide only a broad overview, so we have written this book with three categories of potential readers in mind:

➤ A number of people might have read those stories about neural networks in general-interest magazines as well as in computer magazines, and we hope our book provides the next step for those who are interested in knowing more about the subject.

➤ There might be readers who have read articles and one of the excellent books on the subject. These go into a more detailed overview but do not give technical details. A typical example would be a book like Colin Johnson's and Chappell Brown's *Cognizers*. We hope our book will provide the technical detail such readers seek.

➤ A few years ago, there might have been a substantial number of people who had not come across any references to neural networks. Possibly there are no such people now, but if by chance there are, we would like to interest them, too.

With this target audience in mind, we have adopted the following approach in this book: instead of trying to cover too many aspects of such a vast subject, we have tried to firmly focus on what is generally regarded as the core of the subject—a good understanding of the key models in artificial networks, namely multilayer feedforward networks and Hopfield networks. In the last chapter of this book, we mention some collections of articles that deal with various other models that we have not included. We regard them as more appropriate for the next level of learning about neural networks. Our book is meant to be a stepping stone that could lead interested readers on to more comprehensive and more detailed books. There are many such excellent books, and we would like to recommend our favorite, Stephen Gallant's *Neural Network Learning and Expert Systems*.

For readers who plan to go on to further study of the theory of neural networks in depth, we have provided two appendices, one on matrix algebra and one on statistics, which we hope will provide useful theoretical background for further study.

To enable you to get a real feel for how artificial neural networks operate, we have provided a disk with basic programs related to the key models. The book can be read without using the programs, but we hope trying out the programs will add to your understanding of the basics of neural networks. We hope the companion disk will also please those who are enthusiastic for hands-on experience.

We are very interested in receiving comments or suggestions from readers. We hope that in an expanding field like neural networks, we might have an opportunity in the future to try our hand at a follow-up book that goes to the next level of detailed coverage.

Introduction

This introduction gives an overview of the book by considering the fundamental differences in design and function between computers generally in use and the newer breed of computers called artificial neural networks. Subsequent chapters go into the details of such networks.

Computers play a large and increasing role in all aspects of our lives today. They are valuable tools in a vast variety of applications. Since microcomputers have become available at reasonable prices, millions of us have enjoyed the benefits of word processing and its superiority to typewriters. Another widespread application of computers is searching for information in databases, in libraries, in businesses, and elsewhere. The use of computers for control applications (for example, in hospitals or in spacecraft) is another familiar example of the many, many useful tasks that computers can do.

However, computers have proven relatively less successful in certain tasks such as picture recognition or voice recognition. This has led scientists to investigate alternative principles for designing computers. Computers known as artificial neural networks have achieved considerable success in the last few years and have generated a lot of interest and activity. These computers are based on new design principles. To appreciate what is new about artificial neural networks,

let's start by briefly reviewing the basic principles of what might be called "standard" computers.

Architecture of most computers in use today

What are the fundamental features of computers that enable them to carry out the many, varied tasks they carry out today? Essentially, computers have the following:

> A memory in which relevant information can be electronically coded and stored.

> Instructions about how to solve the particular problem or carry out the task. These instructions can also be coded and stored in the memory of the computer.

> A central processing unit (CPU) that can "fetch" the instructions and data from the memory and carry out the instructions. For obvious reasons, the CPU is often called the "brain" of the computer.

In giving this broad description of a computer, we are, of course, abstracting from a lot of details regarding how the instructions are coded and stored, how they are interpreted and carried out by the CPU, and so on. However, these details are not important for appreciating the significant differences between artificial networks (or connectionist computers as they are sometimes called) and "standard" computers. What is important is that the vast majority of computers in use today, from small personal computers to the giants used for meteorological and other applications, all have the same fundamental design or architecture: a memory that stores instructions and data, and a CPU that carries out those instructions. This fundamental design is often called the *von Neumann design* in honor of the great pioneer of computing, John von Neumann, who was one of the first persons to design a computer based on these principles.

An essential requirement for computers designed in this way is this: they need to have a solution procedure explicitly expressed in terms of logical statements, which they can then carry out. Such a clearly specified procedure is called an *algorithm*. Any problem for which such a procedure can be spelled out is one that can be *effectively* computerized. When such procedures can be spelled out, computers can work much more quickly than human beings, as we all know from our experiences of how computers handle arithmetic, search databases, and so on. The expanding range of computer applications is based on finding ways to express solution procedures for more and more problems in terms of clear, logical statements.

 What computers are not so good at

There is the other side to this requirement. If it is difficult to spell out explicit rules, then it is difficult to computerize the application. Just as the striking successes of computers have been in areas where the rules could be spelled out, their relative lack of success has been in fields where it has not been possible to specify such procedures. For example, it is tough to get computers to recognize pictures. The problem is that it is difficult to find comprehensive, explicit rules to cover the myriad possibilities of distorted pictures, effects of lighting and shade, effects of perspective, and so on. Similarly, trying to computerize voice recognition causes problems because of the variations of tone, accent, etc., which have to be allowed for.

An alternative design: "brain-style" computing

In considering those areas where computerization has proven relatively more difficult, scientists have noted certain extremely interesting characteristics of such problems. They all seem to be problems that people, or we might say, human brains, are able to handle much more effectively than standard computers can. The human brain seems to have an advantage in handling problems where explicit rules are not easily formulated, just as computers have an advantage in areas like arithmetic where such rules can be formulated.

Secondly, the human brain seems to learn such skills not so much by being provided with explicit rules as by learning from examples, using the examples as the basis for extracting or formulating rules of operation. It was natural, therefore, that scientists started investigating the question: is the ability to work without explicit rules and to learn from examples connected with something different about the design or architecture of the components of the brain that carry out information processing?

The working of the human brain is not fully understood, and it is a subject of continuing research. However, to the extent that it is understood today, it seems to operate as follows:

➤ Information processing in the brain is carried out by a network of millions of essentially simple processing units called *neurons*.

➤ The neurons in the human brain are basically simple processors. Essentially, each neuron receives signals from a large number of other neurons, combines these inputs, and then sends out signals to a large number of other neurons. In contrast to this, the CPUs of von Neumann computers are designed to be capable of a complex set or repertoire of actions that they can carry out when given the appropriate command. In chapter 1, we will look in more detail at how an artificial neural network models the way each neuron combines the input it receives, and how its output to other neurons is related to the net input it receives.

➤ In the human brain, there is no equivalent of a CPU that is in overall control of the actions of all of the neurons.

➤ In place of the explicit rules that are used by a standard computer, in the human brain it is the pattern of connections between the neurons that seems to embody the "knowledge" required for carrying out various information-processing tasks. Hence the alternative name, connectionist computing.

Of course, in the preceding brief description of how the brain works, a lot of the details of the complex electrical and chemical processes that go on in the brain have been ignored. It is a very stripped-down conceptual model. The pragmatic justification for such simplification

is that by starting with such a simple model, computer scientists have been able to achieve very useful results.

⇨ So, what are artificial neural networks?

In the context of the issues just discussed, we can now say how artificial neural networks are different from standard computers:

➤ From the point of view of design, artificial neural networks are computing devices that use design principles similar to the design of the information-processing system of the human brain as an alternative to the von Neumann design. The effort is motivated by the hope that such computers will prove more effective than standard computers in tasks where standard computers have problems. As mentioned earlier, artificial neural networks are based on abstracting from the complex details of human brains and building a simple model using a network of simple processors.

➤ From the point of view of function, an important goal is to develop computers that can learn from examples. As we have seen previously, the need for learning from examples is closely related to the difficulty of formulating explicit rules for some applications.

One of the leading scientists in this field, Dr. David Rumelhart, has remarked that, out of the many alternative names such as artificial neural networks or connectionist computing and so on, he thinks the best choice is to refer to the new devices as designed for "brain-style computing." In the following chapters, we will look at more details of how connectionist computers are designed, how they learn, and so on.

The intention is not to replicate the working of the human brain, but to use a simple model to see if some of the strengths of the human brain would be shown by computers based on that model. As we will see in later chapters, there has indeed been very promising progress in getting connectionist computers to learn from examples. Of

course, it is also hoped that the study of simple models of the brain might lead to better understanding of the working of the brain; this, in turn, might lead to better models for connectionist computers . . . and so on in a mutually productive feedback between the two fields.

Different workers in the field have emphasized different aspects. It is possible to make a broad distinction as follows: some efforts have focused more on what might be called the engineering aspects. The primary goal is to see if computers based on the new principles prove more effective in applications where standard computers have had some problems. Other efforts have focused more on the psychological aspects. A major goal of such efforts is to study artificial neural networks as experimental models that throw light on the functioning of the human mind and brain, enable better models to be built, and lead to better understanding of human memory, learning, and so on. But the difference is one of emphasis, and it is not as if there are two mutually exclusive fields of research and development. Efforts and progress in either field also help in regard to the other area.

In the last decade or so, much of the study of artificial neural networks was carried out by simulating the operation of such computers by using standard computers, just as the design of new spacecraft or the consequences of new meteorological theories are simulated on standard computers. As a result of the promising results of such study, now the design of actual computers designed on connectionist principles has become an active field.

It has often been pointed out that "artificial birds" or planes fly without flapping their wings, so why should artificial brains have to be designed based on the structure of real brains? The brief answer to this is really the pragmatic one. As we shall see, the study of computers based on the neural network architecture has shown that they have considerable strength in handling problems that have proven difficult for standard computers to handle. At this stage, scientists are not certain of the essential principle that has to be embodied in an artificial brain. To go back to the analogy with planes, we know that flapping the wings is not an essential principle, but having wings that can be buoyed by the air is. Similarly, it could be

that having interconnections between simple processors is an essential principle, but using chemical and electrical processes for the interactions of the processors, as in the brain, is not an essential principle. At this stage, no one fully knows.

One of the things implicit in the new design is this: the neurons in the human brain are much, much slower than the chips used in standard computers. But the neurons in the human brain seem to work very quickly in various information-processing tasks. The question arises: is this because in a network the units work essentially in *parallel*, with each unit able to carry on various functions at the same time as other units? In contrast, the standard design based on a central processing unit essentially requires actions to be carried out one by one, i.e., *serially* or *sequentially*. This is an issue being investigated not only in regard to artificial neural networks, but also in connection with other designs of computers that try to use a number of CPUs in parallel, instead of using a single CPU.

We refer to the standard architecture of computers as the von Neumann design in contrast to the connectionist design. As further evidence of the genius of von Neumann, we should note that he had given thought to the connectionist design in his writings, and it was his untimely death in 1954 that left his work in this area incomplete. In a sense, the connectionist design is a von Neumann design, too.

Finally, it turns out that in the process of learning from examples, artificial neural networks exhibit another very valuable characteristic. They show a capacity to *generalize*. By that we mean the following: if they have learned to deal with a certain problem, and they are presented with one similar to but not quite the same as the one they have learned, they tend to recognize the new problem as being "close" to the one they know, and they offer the same solution. Of course, this is typically the way we human beings tend to generalize and apply our knowledge to new problems that are similar to ones we already know. To appreciate how exactly this capacity to generalize operates, and to appreciate the differences between standard computers and brain-style computers better, we should first look at some details of how some artificial neural networks operate, and this is what we will do in the next few chapters.

To conclude, it is worth mentioning again that artificial neural networks are not meant to replace or supersede the existing design of computers. They are meant more to complement them. Already, applications in which neural networks and standard programming operate together are emerging in many areas.

Part 1

Principles of neural computing

1

Basics of an
artificial neural network

I N this chapter, we consider the basic concept of computing devices called artificial neural networks or ANNs. We then go on to consider the fundamental building block of ANNs—artificial neurons or ANs. We also further consider the question raised in the previous chapter: how are ANNs different from standard computers, and how and why are the differences significant?

Computers are very useful for simulating existing or proposed systems. A system is made of a number of interacting components, and simulation of a system involves two major steps:

> ➤ Building a conceptual model of the system, specifying the behavior of the components, and formulating the rules governing the interactions of the various parts of the system.

> ➤ Writing a program that will use the specifications to show the behavior of the system or what is called the dynamics of the system.

The results of the simulation allow us to know more about the system, to change its design, and so on. We can think of a simulation as an experiment that enables us to study a system without having to build a physical model. The technique of simulation on a computer is used in a vast variety of fields. To name a few: simulation of the weather in meteorology, simulation of the economy, and simulation of new engineering designs for spacecraft. Simulation is valuable because it enables us to make improvements in the design and performance of systems. In the past few years, systems called artificial neural networks have been extensively simulated, researched, and studied. In some areas of the field, the next stage of actual physical implementation of the systems has also started.

⇨ What is an artificial neural network?

As the name suggests, an *artificial neural network* is a system that consists of a network of interconnected units called artificial neurons. The units are called artificial neurons because of a certain resemblance to the neurons in the human brain. However, they are

not meant to replicate all the electrochemical details of the human brain. The brain provides a model for the design of ANNs. As we go along, we will see the reasons why ANNs are also known by the alternative names *connectionist computing* and *parallel distributed processing*. We will sometimes refer to artificial neurons as just neurons when there is no possibility of confusion with biological neurons.

There are many ways of interconnecting ANs to form a network, so there can be different types of ANNs. They can be different because of either or both of the following:

> ➤ The operating characteristics of the neurons that make up the network can be different in different networks.

> ➤ Neurons can be connected in different patterns to make up the network, as we will see in examples later in the book.

Because the behavior of the network depends on the behavior of the individual neurons, let's start by looking at the individual neurons.

What is an artificial neuron?

At this stage, we can think of an AN as the name for a conceptual device that works as follows. It receives inputs on one or more input lines. We can think of the inputs as electrical signals of different strengths that would be used when the simulated systems are implemented in hardware. Because the strength of each signal can be represented by a number, we can say more abstractly that the AN receives a list of numbers on its input lines. Another useful way of describing this is to say that it receives various patterns of numbers as input. This also implies that the order of the numbers is important. For example, the pattern 10 20 15 received on inputs 1, 2, and 3 is different from the pattern 20 10 15 received on inputs 1, 2, and 3.

It converts the inputs into a net input. There could be many ways of combining a set of inputs, but typically, ANNs form a net input by calculating a weighted sum of the inputs. For example, an AN that receives the three inputs $X1$, $X2$, and $X3$ might combine them into

a net input as follows, attaching weights of 0.25, 0.4, and 0.35 to the three inputs:

$$0.25 * X1 + 0.4 * X2 + 0.35 * X3$$

One of the key questions in the design of ANNs is this: what are the weights that should be used for the inputs of each of the ANs in the network? We will see later how the weights are chosen. More generally, we can think of $w1$, $w2$, $w3$ as the weights attached respectively to inputs $X1$, $X2$, $X3$ . . . and say the net input is:

$$w1 * X1 + w2 * X2 + w3 * X3 . . . .$$

It responds to different net inputs by producing different net outputs. The relationship between the net input and the output is called the *transfer function* of the AN. There could be different functions or relationships that determine what value of output would be produced for a given net input. One of the most widely used type of transfer function is called the sigmoid function, and we will start by considering this function. We can represent an AN as depicted in Fig. 1-1:

Figure 1-1

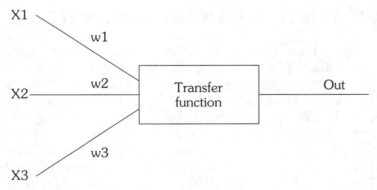

Artificial neuron with three inputs and transfer function.

⇨ Sigmoid function

The sigmoid function relates the output OUT of a neuron to the weighted input or net input IN, which the neuron receives, as follows:

$$OUT = 1 / (1 + exp(- k * IN))$$

In this equation, k is a number that can be chosen to have different values for different neurons. It is referred to as a *parameter* in the equation. The "exp" is the mathematical function known as the *exponential function*, which can be defined in a number of alternative and equivalent ways. Typically, most computer programming languages have a built-in function for calculating the exponential function. One way of defining the exponential function is to say that it is a sum of an infinite series:

$$exp(x) = 1 + x/1! + x**2/ 2! + x**3/ 3! + ...$$

It can also be proven that:

$$exp(x) = e ** x$$

where e is the mathematical constant defined as:

$$e = 1 + 1/ 1! + 1/ 2! + 1 / 3! + ...$$

The sum of this infinite series can be shown to be approximately 2.718281828 . . .

Because the sigmoid function plays a central role in neural networks, you might like to try out the program SIGMOID.EXE, which is provided on the disk. The program asks you to choose a value for the parameter k; then it calculates the value of OUT for different values of IN, and it draws a graph showing the values of IN and OUT. You might like to try using values of k of 0.5, 1, 5, and 10 to replicate Figs. 1-2 to 1-5, and also try other values of k. The results will illustrate the following important properties of the sigmoid function:

➤ It has an S-shaped form: hence the name from sigma for S in Greek.

➤ The value of OUT is always between 0 and 1.

➤ As the parameter k is made larger and larger, the central portion of the graph becomes steeper and steeper. These features are shown in Figs. 1-2 to 1-5.

7

Figure 1-2

Please type in the gain (<= 100):
0.5
x=−5.00 f(x)=0.0759 | +
x=−4.50 f(x)=0.0953 | +
x=−4.00 f(x)=0.1192 | +
x=−3.50 f(x)=0.1480 | +
x=−3.00 f(x)=0.1824 | +
x=−2.50 f(x)=0.2227 | +
x=−2.00 f(x)=0.2689 | +
x=−1.50 f(x)=0.3208 | +
x=−1.00 f(x)=0.3775 | +
x=−0.50 f(x)=0.4378 | +
x= 0.00 f(x)=0.5000 | +
x= 0.50 f(x)=0.5622 | +
x= 1.00 f(x)=0.6225 | +
x= 1.50 f(x)=0.6792 | +
x= 2.00 f(x)=0.7311 | +
x= 2.50 f(x)=0.7773 | +
x= 3.00 f(x)=0.8176 | +
x= 3.50 f(x)=0.8520 | +
x= 4.00 f(x)=0.8808 | +
x= 4.50 f(x)=0.9047 |+ x= 5.00 f(x)=0.9241 |+

Sigmoid function for k = 0.5.

Figure 1-3

Please type in the gain (<= 100):
1
x=−5.00 f(x)=0.0067 |+
x=−4.50 f(x)=0.0110 |+
x=−4.00 f(x)=0.0180 | +
x=−3.50 f(x)=0.0293 | +
x=−3.00 f(x)=0.0474 | +
x=−2.50 f(x)=0.0759 | +
x=−2.00 f(x)=0.1192 | +
x=−1.50 f(x)=0.1824 | +
x=−1.00 f(x)=0.2689 | +
x=−0.50 f(x)=0.3775 | +
x= 0.00 f(x)=0.5000 | +
x= 0.50 f(x)=0.6225 | +
x= 1.00 f(x)=0.7311 | +
x= 1.50 f(x)=0.8176 | +
x= 2.00 f(x)=0.8808 | +
x= 2.50 f(x)=0.9241 | +
x= 3.00 f(x)=0.9526 | +
x= 3.50 f(x)=0.9707 | +
x= 4.00 f(x)=0.9820 | +
x= 4.50 f(x)=0.9890 | +
x= 5.00 f(x)=0.9933 | +

Sigmoid function for k = 1.

Figure 1-4

```
Please type in the gain (<= 100):
5
x=-5.00 f(x)=0.0000 | +
x=-4.50 f(x)=0.0000 | +
x=-4.00 f(x)=0.0000 | +
x=-3.50 f(x)=0.0000 | +
x=-3.00 f(x)=0.0000 | +
x=-2.50 f(x)=0.0000 | +
x=-2.00 f(x)=0.0000 | +
x=-1.50 f(x)=0.0006 | +
x=-1.00 f(x)=0.0067 | +
x=-0.50 f(x)=0.0759 |     +
x=  0.00 f(x)=0.5000 |              +
x=  0.50 f(x)=0.9241 |                   +
x=  1.00 f(x)=0.9933 |                       +
x=  1.50 f(x)=0.9994 |                       +
x=  2.00 f(x)=  1.000 |                       +
x=  2.50 f(x)=  1.000 |                       +
x=  3.00 f(x)=  1.000 |                       +
x=  3.50 f(x)=1.0000 |                       +
x=  4.00 f(x)=1.0000 |                       +
x=  4.50 f(x)=1.0000 |                       +
x=  5.00 f(x)=1.0000 |                       +
```

Sigmoid function for k = 5.

Figure 1-5

```
Please type in the gain (<= 100):
10
x=-5.00 f(x)=0.0000 | +
x=-4.50 f(x)=0.0000 | +
x=-4.00 f(x)=0.0000 | +
x=-3.50 f(x)=0.0000 | +
x=-3.00 f(x)=0.0000 | +
x=-2.50 f(x)=0.0000 | +
x=-2.00 f(x)=0.0000 | +
x=-1.50 f(x)=0.0000 | +
x=-1.00 f(x)=0.0000 | +
x=-0.50 f(x)=0.0067 | +
x=  0.00 f(x)=0.5000 |              +
x=  0.50 f(x)=0.9933 |                     +
x=  1.00 f(x)=  1.000 |                     +
x=  1.50 f(x)=  1.000 |                     +
x=  2.00 f(x)=  1.000 |                     +
x=  2.50 f(x)=1.0000 |                     +
x=  3.00 f(x)=1.0000 |                     +
x=  3.50 f(x)=1.0000 |                     +
x=  4.00 f(x)=1.0000 |                     +
x=  4.50 f(x)=1.0000 |                     +
x=  5.00 f(x)=1.0000 |                     +
```

Sigmoid function for k = 10.

 # Hard threshold function

As we saw previously, when the parameter k is made very large, the sigmoid function tends to the following form. If the weighted or net input of the AN is greater than or equal to 0, it produces an output of 1. Otherwise, it will not produce any output, or we can say that it will produce an output of strength 0.

We can say that the transfer function now has a threshold of 0. At and above the threshold, the neuron produces an output of 1, and otherwise no output at all. Because of the abrupt change at the threshold, this transfer function is called a *hard* threshold.

More generally, this hard threshold can be adjusted to have a threshold other than 0, which we will call T, as shown in Fig. 1-6. We can say that the AN "fires" if it receives a net input greater than or equal to T; otherwise it does not fire. To the left of the AN, two *input nodes* are also shown. They receive the inputs and pass them on to the AN without any change. The reason we have put in the input nodes is because later, we will look at networks of ANs. It is convenient to have each of the inputs come to a node and get passed on from there to each of the ANs that is to receive that input. We can also think of it broadly as something like the retina of the eye receiving various signals in an "input layer" and then passing them on to cells in the brain for processing.

Figure 1-6

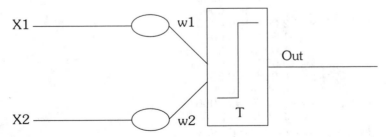

McCulloch-Pitts neuron with two inputs and hard threshold T.

Historically, the concept of an AN with a hard threshold was introduced by the two scientists, Warren McCulloch and Walter Pitts,

in the early 1940s. Their aim was to build a mode to show how the brain could carry out logical functions. In honor of them, a neuron of this type is called a *McCulloch-Pitts neuron*, or MP neuron for short.

⇨ What can an MP neuron compute?

Let's first consider an AN with two inputs, where the inputs are of a very simple type. Instead of receiving signals of various possible strengths on its input lines, this simple AN receives either a standard signal strength, or does not receive any signal. We can describe this by saying its input on any input line can be either 1 or 0. In terms of patterns of inputs, the four possible patterns it can receive are 0 0, 0 1, 1 0, and 1 1. We saw that for the AN to fire, its net input must be greater than or equal to its threshold. The net input is the weighted sum of the two inputs $X1$ and $X2$, and for the neuron to fire we need:

$$w1 * X1 + w2 * X2 >= T$$

Each of the inputs $X1$ and $X2$ is either 0 or 1; $w1$ and $w2$ are the weights attached to the inputs, and T is the threshold. For the pairs of inputs 0 and 0, 1 and 0, 0 and 1, and 1 and 1, this equation for the neuron to fire reduces respectively to:

$$0 > = T$$

$$w1 > = T$$

$$w2 > = T$$

$$w1 + W2 > = T$$

We see that if we choose T to be a positive number, and we decide that each of the weights $w1$ and $w2$ is a positive number less than T, then when the AN is fed any of the patterns 0 0 or 0 1 or 1 0, it will not fire or produce an output. But if $w1$ and $w2$ are such that $w1 + w2$ is greater than or equal to T, when the 11 is received, the AN will fire.

In other words, by properly choosing $w1$, $w2$, and T when designing the AN, we can give it the capability to differentiate between the pattern 1 1 and the set of three patterns 0 0, 0 1, and 1 0.

Again, suppose we choose $w1$ and $w2$ so that each of them is at least equal to T; we see that the AN will fire when it detects the patterns 0 1 and 1 0 and 1 1, but it will not fire when it "sees" the pattern 0 0. With this different choice of weights and threshold, it makes a different kind of distinction or demarcation between the four possible patterns at its input. In Fig. 1-7, the four patterns are shown as points on a graph. In terms of this graph, we can say that depending on the way the weights and threshold are chosen, the AN draws a "line of demarcation" separating 1 1 from the other three, or separating 0 0 from the other three. In the next chapter, we will go into more detail regarding these lines of demarcation.

Figure 1-7

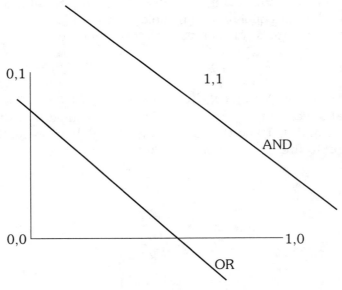

Lines of demarcation: OR line separates 00 from the other three; AND line separates 11 from the other three.

Let's describe this process in another way. When it fires for 1 1 but not for the other patterns, we can say that it fires when input 1 AND

input 2 are both active, but not when only one or neither is active. Similarly, when it does not fire for 0 0 but fires for all the others, we can say it fires when input 1 OR input 2 is active, or when both are active. This way of describing the AN makes it a *logic gate* because it is in effect implementing the logical concepts of AND and OR: When a signal is at level 1, it is treated as TRUE; when it is at level 0 it is treated as FALSE. Next, suppose we design an AN with a threshold of 0 and with only one input, and we give this input a negative weight. We see that the AN will fire when the input line is not active because the net input is then 0, and this equals the threshold. But when the input line becomes active, the net input is negative and is below the threshold of 0, so the neuron will not fire. We can describe this in two ways. We can say the input "inhibits" the neuron. Alternatively, we can say the AN is implementing the logical concept of NOT: it fires when the input is not active or NOT TRUE. Thinking of the AN as a device that implements the logical operations of AND, OR, and NOT leads to ways of designing ANs so that they can distinguish patterns and classify them.

At this stage, it might be useful for you to try out the program MCPITTS in the disk at the back of the book, which allows you to choose different values of $w1$, $w2$, and T. By experimenting with different values, you can see how you can adjust them so that the neuron fires when input 1 AND input 2 are active, when input 1 OR input 2 is active, or when both are active. The program also allows you to study how an AN implements the NOT logical operation. Because the threshold can also be varied, it is convenient to rewrite the previous equation in a slightly modified way:

$$w1 * X1 + w2 * X2 - T * 1 >= 0$$

This is equivalent to treating the AN as always having an input of 1 in addition to other inputs, this steady input having an adjustable weight of $-T$ applied to it and always having a threshold of 0. This steady input of 1 is often designated as $X0$, and the weight $-T$, which is attached to it, is represented as $w0$. So the equation can be written as:

$$w1 * X1 + w2 * X2 + w0 * X0 > = 0$$

...ch and Pitts are regarded as the distinguished pioneers in this
...ause of their insights:

➤ That the neurons in the brain can be regarded as logic gates.

➤ That the information processing capability of the brain (and in particular its ability to operate with the logical functions AND, OR, and NOT) could be explained using such a model.

⇨ Why use an ANN?

We saw previously that an AN can compute the complete set of logical functions AND, OR, and NOT. It follows that by combining a number of such ANs into a network, we can compute anything that can be computed by a standard computer; we know that a standard computer is based on connecting up a large number of logic gates, and that is precisely what we have with a network of ANs. The question then arises: what, if any, are the advantages of having a network of ANs if what they compute is the same as what standard computers compute?

A very important difference is this: In the case of a standard computer, a precise program of instructions has to be given for the computer to get from the given input to the desired output or solution of the problem. ANNs have a capability that makes them significantly different. They can learn from examples. If they are provided with pairs of data in which the first member of the pair is a given pattern of input and the second member is the desired output, the ANN can be "trained" to adjust its weights so that it associates the correct answer with each input. This capability is important because there are many problems in which you know what should be the correct result, but it is not possible to lay down a precise procedure or set of rules for finding the result. In such cases, if providing examples will enable the ANN to develop its own implicit rules in terms of the correct weights to use, it is certainly advantageous.

The pairs of data, input, and corresponding desired output that are used to train the neural network are called the *training set* of data—a term you will encounter a number of times in the rest of this book.

Let's illustrate this by a simple example with just one AN. We want it to learn the AND function (i.e., we want it to adjust its weights so that if it is presented with any of the three input patterns 0 0 or 0 1 or 1 0, it will say "no" or FALSE and output a 0, and if it is presented with the pattern 1 1 it will say "yes" or TRUE and output a 1. We need, of course, to provide the AN with a learning rule that tells it how to adjust its weights if the weights it starts out with produce the wrong answers. Suppose we start off the AN with the weights 0.5 and 0.6 for the two inputs, and 0.3 for the threshold.

For example, its net input is:

$$0.5 * X1 + 0.6 * X2 - 0.3 * X0$$

where X0 is the steady input always set at 1, as discussed earlier. The AN fires or does not fire depending on whether the net input is greater than or equal to 0 or not.

We see that the net inputs for the four possible patterns are:

0 0	−0.3
1 0	0.2
0 1	0.3
1 1	0.8

So it will output 1 for all the patterns 0 1, 1 0, and 1 1, whereas we want it to output 1 only for the input pattern 1 1. The learning rule usually applied is intuitively reasonable and prescribes the following adjustments:

❶ Present one of the input patterns and let the AN produce an output using its current weights.

❷ If the output is the same as the desired output, go back to step 1 using the next input pattern.

❸ If the output is 0 and the desired output is 1, increase the weight associated with each of the active input lines, i.e., those that are

at level 1. Make the amount of increase some fraction of the error. We see that the error is 1 (it is a 0 instead of 1), so increase the weights on the active input lines by say 0.1. It makes sense to increase the weights on the active input lines because we want to increase the output. Also, clearly there is no point in changing the weights on the inactive input lines (those that are at level 0) because they are not contributing anything to the output.

❹ By the same line of reasoning, if the output is 1 and the desired output is 0, the weights are decreased for the active input lines.

❺ Repeat the adjusted process in turn for each of the input patterns.

It is not obvious that making these adjustments repeatedly for each input pattern in turn will lead to a situation where the weights will reach a state where the correct desired output will be produced for all of the input patterns (i.e., the ANN will learn the correct answers). It is regarded as one of the great theoretical advances that Frank Rosenblatt, a distinguished pioneer in this field, proved that if there is a solution to the problem, then the correct weights will be found in a finite number of adjustments. That "if" is important, as we will see later: there are problems for which there is no solution, and so the adjustments will not lead to a solution.

The learning rule as previously outlined is a later refinement of the original rule used by Rosenblatt. The modified rule is often called the *Widrow-Hoff rule* or the *generalized delta rule*. The process of finding the solution is described by saying that the weights will converge to the correct solution. Rosenblatt referred to his version of ANs as *perceptrons*, and the model we have been considering is sometimes referred to as a single perceptron.

Now let's see how the adjustment or learning rules should be applied in the previous example. Our starting pattern of weights is:

$$0.5 \quad 0.6 \quad -0.3$$

We give the AN the input 0 0. The net input is -0.3, which is less than 0. It produces the correct output 0, so we go on to the next input pattern.

We give it the input pattern 1 0. It produces the output 1 because the net input:

$$0.5 * 1 + 0.6 * 0 - 0.3 * 1 = 0.2 \text{ is greater than or equal to } 0$$

This is a case where the output is greater than the desired output. So we have to adjust the weights of the active lines downward, by a fraction 0.1 of the error. So we adjust the weights to get a new pattern:

$$0.4 \quad 0.6 \quad \text{and} \quad -0.4$$

The second weight is not adjusted because that input was inactive. We go on to the next input pattern, 0 1. Using the new weights, the net input is now:

$$0.4 * 0 + 0.6 * 1 - 0.4 = 0.2$$

This is greater than 0, so the output is 1, which is not the correct output. So, an adjustment of weights is necessary. We adjust the weights of the active inputs downward by 0.1 to get the new pattern of weights:

$$0.4 \quad 0.5 \quad -0.5$$

We go on to the next input pattern: 1 1. The net input now is:

$$0.4 * 1 + 0.5 * 1 - 0.5 * 1 = 0.4$$

Because this is more than 0, the output is 1, which is the desired output. So there is no need to adjust any weights. We cycle back and test 0 0. The net input is −0.5, and the output is 0, which is the correct output.

We test 1 0. The net input is −0.1, so the output is 0, which is the correct output. We go on to the next input pattern, 0 1. The net input is −0 and the output is 1, which is not the correct output. So we need to make a downward adjustment to get the new pattern of weights:

$$0.4 \quad 0.4 \quad -0.6$$

We go on to the next input pattern, 1 1. The net input is 0.2, which produces an output of 1; that is the correct output.

We go back and test if the output is correct for 0 0 and 1 0 and 0 1. It is. So, we have reached a new set of weights that do produce the correct output for all inputs:

$$0.4 \quad 0.4 \quad \text{and} \quad -0.6$$

If we draw the line $0.4 \times 1 + 0.4 \times 2 = 0.6$, we see in Fig. 1-8 that it does separate the set of point 0 0, 1 0, and 0 1 from the point 1 1.

Figure 1-8

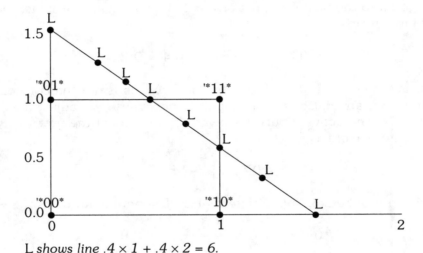

L shows line $.4 \times 1 + .4 \times 2 = 6$.

Theoretically, the successive adjustments could take a number of steps before the system learns all the correct answers. The number of steps taken also depends on what fraction of the error is used for correcting weights. We have used a fraction 0.1, and the number of steps would be different if we use a different fraction. Also, at this stage we have considered the simplest case, where the inputs and outputs are only 0 or 1. There are alternative designs in which the values of the inputs and outputs are not restricted to 0 or 1.

However, before we go on to consider these alternative designs, it would be useful for you to try out the program LEARNIT at the back

of the book. This program allows you to choose some arbitrary weights to start with, and it also allows you to choose different fractions of the error to use for adjusting the weights. You might want to try out the program first using the weights and error correction fraction 0.1 from the previous example; then try using different fractions for error correction.

⇨ What next?

In this chapter, we saw the operation of a single MP neuron using a hard threshold. As mentioned earlier, neurons can have transfer functions differently from a hard threshold. Principally, sigmoid functions with $k = 1$ have been used extensively, and we will study these in the next chapter.

Also, in this chapter we considered only a single neuron, and we saw that it can compute the basic logical functions AND, OR, and NOT. Most important of all, we saw that a neuron can learn from examples. However, single neurons have some limitations. In the next chapter, we will consider what these limitations are. We will also consider the different ways in which ANs can be interconnected to form networks and how such networks can overcome some of the limitations of single neurons.

Multilayer
feedforward networks

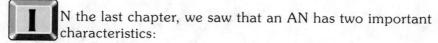

I N the last chapter, we saw that an AN has two important characteristics:

➤ It can classify input patterns and categorize them. The examples we saw of an AN implementing an AND logical function was equivalent to its classifying the pattern 1 1 as different from the others. Similarly, the OR function was the same as classifying 0 0 in one category and the others in a different category.

➤ An AN can "learn from examples." It can adjust its weights using a simple learning rule to get the desired results that are presented to it.

These characteristics are obviously useful for applications such as recognition of pictures by classifying them in terms of characteristic features. However, inherent in the way an AN works is a limitation on what it can classify.

⇨ Linearly separable sets

In the examples we considered in the last chapter, we saw that, essentially, an AN recognizes different categories by adjusting the weights so that for one category:

$$w1 * X1 + w2 * X2 >= T$$

Or equivalently:

$$w1 * X1 + w2 * X2 + w0 * X0 >= 0$$

And for the other category:

$$w1 * X1 + w2 * X2 < T \text{ or } w1 * X1 + w2 * X2 + w0 * X0 < 0$$

where T is the threshold, and $wo = -T$ is the weight for the constant input of $X0 = 1$, which is often called the *bias*. (In what follows, we will refer to $w0$ as $-T$ or to T as $-w0$ as necessary.)

Linear combination of the variables is another name for the weighted sum of a set of variables that is found on the left-hand side of the above inequalities. It is a standard result in algebra that if we form a linear combination of two variables and set it as equal to some number, then the points in the two-dimensional "space" or surface of the paper can be divided into three categories:

➤ All the points on the line will have:

$$w1 * X1 + w2 * X2 = T$$

➤ All the points on one side of the line will have:

$$w1 * X1 + w2 * X2 < T$$

➤ All the points on the other side of the line will have:

$$w1 * X1 + w2 * X2 > T$$

For example, if we draw a line $2 * X1 + 3 * X2 = 6$, we can see that for all points on the line, the value of the linear combination is exactly equal to 6. For all points below the line, it is less than 6, and for all lines above the line it is greater than 6. Figures 2-1A and 2-1B show some selected points and the values of the linear combination at these points.

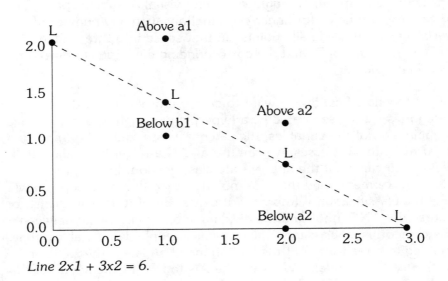

Line 2x1 + 3x2 = 6.

Figure 2-1A

2-1B

Point	Value of 2x1 + 3x2 = 6	Above on or below
1 ,2	8	Above a1
2, 1	7	Above a2
1, 1	5	Below b1
2, 0	4	Below b2
0, 2	6	On L
1, 1.333...	6	On L
2, 0.666...	6	On L
3, 0	6	On L

Line 2x1 + 3x2 = 6 and selected points on, above, or below the line, with a value of 2x1 + 3x2 for each point.

Similarly, if we have three variables, a linear combination like

$$w1 * X1 + w2 * X2 + w3 * X3 = T$$

would be a plane, and this plane would divide the three-dimensional space into three categories as in the two-dimensional example. Metaphorically, any particular set of values for, say, 5 variables, $X1$, $X2$, $X3$, $X4$, and $X5$ is referred to as a "point in five-dimensional space or hyperspace," though we cannot visualize such a space. The same property holds for linear combinations with any number of variables. They divide all "points" in that space into three categories of $= T$, $< T$, and $> T$, and the corresponding equation is referred to as a *hyperplane*.

When the classification we want to carry out is such that the categories can be separated by a hyperplane, weighted sum, or linear combination of the variables, the categories are said to be *linearly separable*. In such cases, we can use an AN and get it to adjust its weights to carry out the appropriate classification. In the previous chapter, we mentioned that Rosenblatt proved that a perceptron will find the classification if (repeat if) it exists. But if it does not exist, of course the AN cannot find the dividing line or hyperplane between the categories. A classic example, involving only two variables, that first led to a realization of the limitations of an AN is the XOR or *exclusive OR problem*. We want the AN to fire if exactly one of the inputs is on or at level 1, but not when both are on. We saw in the

last chapter that the inclusive OR, i.e., one or both of the inputs being on, is easily implemented by an AN. We can see the problem with an exclusive OR by looking at Fig. 2-2.

Figure 2-2

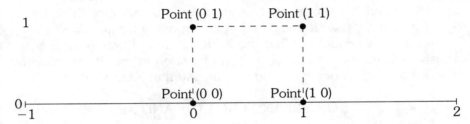

XOR—not linearly separable.

It is clear that no linear combination or straight line can be drawn so as to put 0,0 and 1,1 in one category and 1,0 and 0,1 in the other category. We can see this impossibility by looking at the situation algebraically. We want:

$$w1 * 1 + w2 * 0 >= T$$

for point (1,0), and

$$w1 * 0 + w2 * 1 >= T$$

for point (0,1)

But adding these together gives

$$w1 * 1 + w2 * 1 >= T$$

which means that (1,1) will be on the same side of the line, which we do not want. (Please think of the following: What if we choose weights so that (1,0) and (0,1) are on the < side of

$$w1 * X1 + w2 * X2 = T$$

25

and (1,1) and (0,0) are on the > side? Why will this not work either?) Analogous situations involving more variables where the categories are not linearly separable would again be beyond the capability of an AN.

⇨ **Multilayer perceptrons**

The XOR function is beyond the capacity of a single AN. However, we saw that a single AN essentially carries out any of the logical functions AND, OR, or NOT. So, if some function beyond the capability of an AN can be expressed as a combination of these basic logical functions, then it could be implemented by using more ANs. For instance, we could say that the XOR function differs from the inclusive OR (one or the other or both) function in that it excludes the case of both inputs being on. So we can say that XOR is:

$$(X1 \text{ OR } X2) \text{ AND } (\text{ NOT } (X1 \text{ AND } X2))$$

So, if we get one AN to do the INCLUSIVE OR ($X1$ or $X2$ or both), others to do the NOT ($X1$ AND $X2$), and another to do the AND of these two, the exclusive OR can be implemented. A way of doing these, using appropriate weights, is shown in Fig. 2-3. It shows a network with two processing layers, and we can think of the demarcation it has made as equivalent to drawing two lines, AB and CD, as shown in Fig. 2-4. Between them, these two lines carve out the area ABCD, which contains the points 1 0 and 0 1 and distinguishes them from the other points 0 0 and 1 1.

Now let's generalize about what we have just seen. We have considered the simple case where inputs and outputs to a neuron are binary, either 0 or 1. But, as mentioned in the previous chapter, neural networks also use units whose inputs and outputs can be any number. Typically, they are scaled to be any number in the range 0 to 1. In such cases, if a neuron has two inputs, they are any two numbers in the range from 0 to 1. Any pair of such numbers can be represented by a point on the boundary or inside the square with 0 0, 1 0, 1 1, and 0 1 as its corners. For instance, the pattern or pair of numbers (0.33, 0.48) would be such a point. In the case of such input patterns, a single unit "draws a line" that separates the infinite number of possible patterns of pairs of numbers on each side of the line.

Figure 2-3

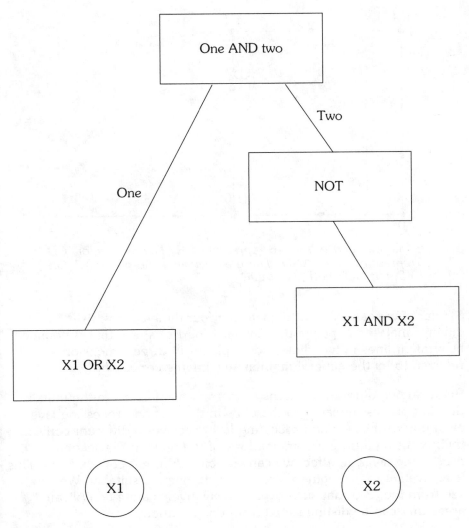

Two-layer network for XOR.

We can put into the first processing layer two, three, four . . . units, each of which draws its own line. In the next processing layer, we can separate out any part of the square that can be bounded by straight lines. We can carve out a triangle or a quadrilateral, and so on. In the case of three inputs, we can think of the area carved out by the units as a block in three dimensions bounded on all sides by planes.

27

Figure 2-4

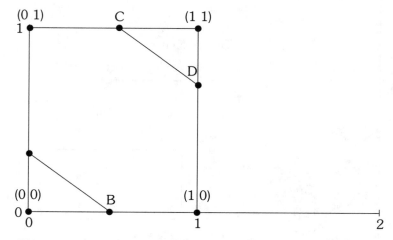

The area above line AB represents OR. The area below CD represents NOT AND. The area between the two is X1 OR X2, but NOT both, i.e., XOR.

Similarly, we can extend the idea to a four-dimensional, five-dimensional, etc., "polygon." Any such part of space that is bounded by straight lines in two dimensions, planes in three dimensions . . . is referred to by the general mathematical name *convex hull*.

By arranging different patterns of interconnections from the units in the first processing layer to the units in the second processing layer, each unit of the second processing layer receives a different convex hull. By using different combinations of the units in the second processing layer, in effect we can combine different convex hulls. This is equivalent to arranging these figures to overlap suitably. We can see from Fig. 2-5 that such overlaps will give us quite complicated areas that can be distinguished from one another.

The analogous results for more variables or dimensions are also true. The argument just discussed is an intuitive explanation of an important theoretical result called *Kolmogorov's theorem*. This theorem says, in essence, that two layers of processing units would be sufficient for carving out any kind of linearly nonseparable demarcation we want. However, Kolmogorov's theorem only shows the minimum number of processing layers required. So, in practice, suitable solutions are worked out sometimes using two processing layers, sometimes more.

Figure 2-5

Overlapped convex areas can lead to quite complicated regions of demarcation.

ANs can be combined into a network in many different ways. What we will consider next are networks in which the ANs are arranged in layers and the output of any layer goes only to subsequent layers and not to earlier layers. Such an arrangement is called a *multilayer feedforward network*. This is one of the most widely used pattern of connections. However, there are other types of networks as well. When ANs send their output back to ANs from which they have received input, the pattern of connections is known, for obvious reasons, as a network with *feedback*. Another name for such a network is *recurrent network*. There are some other types of network structures as well.

Within the class of multilayered feedforward networks, we can again distinguish two types. A network of this type is called *strictly layered* if the output from a unit goes only to units in the very next layer. On the other hand, if it is just layered and not strictly layered, the output from a unit could go forward to the next layer, or to the next-but-one layer . . . and so on, skipping one or more layers, though it still goes only forward through the various layers.

Problem of training multilayer networks

Though the limitation of linear separability for single ANs can be overcome by using more layers, there was one fundamental problem

about multilayered networks that caused a slowing down of research and development in the neural network field after the concept of multilayered networks was first developed in the 1960s. The problem was that there seemed to be no guaranteed learning rule that could be used to "train" the network, e.g., get it to adjust the weights throughout the network.

We saw, in the case of the perceptron or single AN, that the rule for adjusting the weights had been proven by Rosenblatt and others as guaranteed to find the correct weights if they existed. But no similar learning rules and results were forthcoming for multilayer perceptrons. This, coupled with the fact that there was very encouraging progress in other fields of artificial intelligence, led to relatively less progress in the neural network field.

However, in the mid-1980s David Rumelhart and others developed a learning rule that has become the workhorse of neural networks. Historically, the rule had been discovered earlier by Paul Werbos and others, but the resurgence of activity in the neural networks field was stimulated by the work of Rumelhart and his colleagues. We will now look at this method of training multilayer feedforward networks—a method known as the *backpropagation* method.

⇨ What is backprop?

The reason that the method is called backpropagation is this: the method is based on finding the outputs at the last or output layer of the network and calculating the errors or differences between the desired outputs and the current outputs. This is similar to what we saw in the case of the single AN. When the output was different from the desired output, corrections were made in the weights, in proportion to the error or discrepancy between the desired output and the actual output. However, in the case of the multilayer network, corrections have to be made for the weights from the first to the second layer, the second to the third layer . . . the last-but-one layer to the last or output layer.

The basic problem is that any changes in these weights has a chain of effects that propagates forward through the succeeding layers of the network. So all these effects have to be taken into account. The theory of the backpropagation method, which we will look at in detail, involves making the corrections to the weights from the last-but-one layer to the last layer first, then using the calculations involved in these corrections as the basis for calculating the corrections for the next layer back . . . until the input layer is reached. Hence the name backprop. To understand the concepts that underlie the method and make it clear why it is necessary to proceed backwards, we need first to look at two preliminary concepts.

⇨ Some preliminaries for backprop

We saw in the last chapter that one of the transfer functions that is used for ANs is the sigmoid function:

$$OUT = 1/ (1 + \exp(- k * IN))$$

For many applications, the parameter k is set at the value 1. An important characteristic of the sigmoid function that is helpful to keep in mind when looking at how the backpropagation method works is the following: at any level of IN and OUT, if the weighted input IN is increased by a very small quantity that we denote by h, then the output OUT will increase by a quantity:

$$h * OUT * (1 - OUT) * k$$

Because k is typically set at 1, in what follows we will assume we are dealing with networks with that value of k.

Equivalently, we can say that the rate at which output changes for small changes in input, i.e., change in output divided by change in input:

$$= OUT * (1 - OUT)$$

This is also described by saying that the coefficient of response of the output of any unit n to changes in the input is

$$OI(n) = OUT(n) * (1 - OUT(n))$$

with OI standing for increase in OUTPUT/ increase in INPUT, and with the understanding that we are considering small changes in input. (Readers acquainted with the differential calculus will recognize that we are dealing with the first derivative of the output with respect to the input.) To get a feel for this important characteristic of the sigmoid transfer function, you might like to experiment with the program SIGRESP, which is available on the disk.

It would be useful to look at another preliminary before we get to the details of the backprop method. Consider a multilayer feedforward network as shown in Fig. 2-6. In this example, we have three input ports that receive input signals whose levels we indicate by $X1$, $X2$, and $X3$. This layer does not do any processing. It merely distributes or fans out the inputs to the first processing layer consisting of units 4, 5, and 6. These in turn pass on their outputs to the second processing layer of units 7 and 8. These are also the output units that send outputs (which we will call $X7$ and $X8$) out of the network. The layers between the input ports and the output layer are called *hidden layers* because they do not directly receive inputs from or send outputs to anywhere outside the network. In this example, we have only one hidden layer, but there can be more than one such layer in more complex networks.

Also, as mentioned earlier, sometimes a network is referred to in terms of how many processing layers there are. The previous example would be called a two-layer network. Sometimes the input layer is also included, and this would be called a three-layer network. But increasingly it seems more common to count only the processing layers and not the input layer.

The final outputs from the network will be from the neurons in the last or output layer, and let's say that the target or desired outputs for these are $r7$ and $r8$, where r is used to remind us it is the required response. Suppose that, with some randomly chosen pattern of weights we use to start with, the actual outputs are $X7$ and $X8$. The errors in the outputs are respectively said to be: $r7 - X7$ and $r8 - X8$. They are measured in terms of how much the actual output falls short of the desired output. The error is positive if the actual output is less than the target output or required response.

Figure 2-6

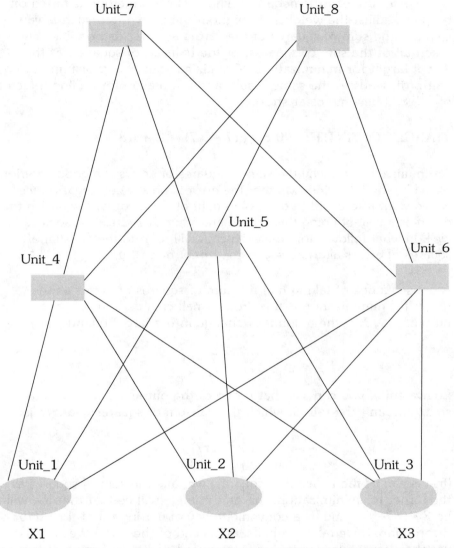

Unit_7   Unit_8

Unit_5

Unit_4   Unit_6

Unit_1   Unit_2   Unit_3

X1   X2   X3

Multilayer feedforward network with one hidden layer. Units 1, 2, and 3 are the input layer; the inputs X1, X2, and X3 are distributed or fanned out to the hidden layer. Units 4, 5, and 6 are the first processing layer—a hidden layer. Units 7 and 8 are the output layer

Otherwise, the error is negative. The backprop method is based on trying to adjust the weights throughout the network in such a way as to make the sum of squares of the errors as small as possible. We take half of the sum of squares, or the halfsum of squares, as the actual target for minimization. Minimizing something, or minimizing half of it, leads to the same result, and the reason for adding a factor of 0.5 will become clear shortly:

TARGET QUANTITY = $0.5 * ((r7 - X7) ** 2 + (r8 - X8) ** 2 + ...)$

An intuitive reason why the sum of squares of errors is a good criterion would be the following: whether the error is positive or negative, we would want it to count in our assessment of the error, and squaring the errors is a way of doing this. There are other theoretical reasons as well. In what follows, for convenience, I will refer to the halfsum of squares of errors alternatively as the *target quantity*.

A consequence of taking half the sum of squares of errors as the target for minimization is this. For a small change h in one of the outputs, say $X7$, the amount of change in the target quantity is:

$$(X7 - r7) * h$$

Equivalently, you can say that if one of the outputs changes by a small amount, the rate at which the halfsum of squares changes is:

$$(X7 - r7)$$

(If, instead of the halfsum of squares, we take the sum of squares as the target for minimization, the only change will be that the rate will be $2 * (X7 - r7)$, and as a convenient way of getting rid of the factor of 2 throughout, we take the halfsum instead of the sum.) We can also use the alternative terminology introduced earlier and say that the *coefficient of response* of the halfsum of squares of errors with respect to changes in output is $(X7 - r7)$.

We can see from this that:

> If the output is too high, i.e., $X7$ is more than the required response $r7$, the coefficient of response is a positive number. We need to reduce $X7$ or make a negative change in $X7$ so that the negative change h in $X7$ times the positive coefficient of response will lead to a reduction in the target quantity.

> If the output is too low, i.e., $X7$ is less than $r7$, the coefficient of response $X7 - r7$ is a negative number.

We need to increase $X7$ so that the positive change h in $X7$ times the negative coefficient of response will lead to a reduction in the target quantity. In the same way as for unit or neuron 7, the rate of change of the halfsum of squares of errors with respect to changes in output of neuron or unit 8 is:

$$(X8 - r8)$$

. . . and so on. To get a feel for this, you might like at this stage to experiment with the program SUMSQ, which is on the disk.

Another concept we need to consider is derived from the theory of differential calculus and is known as the *gradient descent technique*. The essence of the theory is that sometimes something we want to minimize has rates of change or coefficients of response with respect to a number of factors or variables. (In this example, the target quantity has responses to changes in either or both of the output $X7$ and the output $X8$.) When this is the case, then the most efficient method is to make changes in all of these factors in the same proportion of their respective coefficients of response. We should aim to change both $X7$ and $X8$ by some proportion of the coefficient of response of the target quantity with respect to changes in these two variables. In the backpropagation method, we are going to change the outputs of units 7 and 8 by changing their inputs by adjusting the weights $w47$, $w48$, $w57$, $w58$, $w67$, and $w68$. So we need to know the coefficients of response of the target quantity with respect to changes in these weights. Moreover, we want also to change the other weights in the network, $w14$, $w15$, $w16$ . . . so we need to know the coefficients of response with respect to changes in all of these as well.

⇨ How the error corrections are propagated backward

In considering why the backpropagation method requires proceeding backward through the network, we will use the preliminary concepts just discussed. Let's say we have a network with an input layer and a number of processing layers, say 6, of which the last is the output layer. We measure the outputs at the last layer, and if it is not the same as the desired output, we would like to adjust the weights throughout the network to reduce the difference between the desired and actual outputs.

Let's start by considering the weight between say unit 1 in the input layer or layer 0 and unit 5 in the first processing layer or layer 1. Any change we make in the weight connecting them, $w15$, will change the weighted input of unit 5 because it receives $w15 * X1$ from unit 1. Consequently, the output of unit 5 will be changed. We know the output of unit 5 will be fed to all the units in the next layer, layer 2. So, to estimate the effect on the error of any change in $w15$ and consequently in the input provided by it to unit 5, we need to know the effect on the error of changes in the inputs of all the units in layer 2.

Again, to know the effect on the error of changes in the inputs of units in layer 2, we need to know how the error will change in response to the changes in the inputs provided to units in layer 3 from the units in layer 2. This in turn requires estimating the response of the error to changes in the inputs of units in layer 4 . . . and so on. In other words, to know how the error will change in response to changes in the weights connecting a unit to any unit in the next layer, we need to know the behavior of units in all subsequent layers. It logically follows that we need to first study the last or output layer, then use this to estimate the behavior of the last-but-one layer, then use this to study the behavior of the layer before that . . . and so on.

⇨ Illustration with two-layer network

Having looked at the logic of why you have to work backward from the last layer, let's consider the application of the method to a

two-layer network as shown in Fig. 2-6. The steps in applying the backprop method are as follows:

❶ Some test pattern of inputs X1, X2, X3 would be applied at the input nodes of the network in Fig. 2-6. The various layers will process the input and produce a final output of X7 and X8 at the two output nodes. The targets or desired outputs might be r7 and r8 so that there are errors of r7 − X7 and r8 − X8.

❷ We would like to adjust the weights throughout the network so as to minimize half the sum of squares of errors. According to the gradient descent method, we need to make the changes proportional to the coefficients of response.

 # Adjustment of weights in layer just before output layer

Suppose we start at the output layer of the network and consider the question: How should we adjust any of these weights, say $w47$, so that the sum of squares of errors at the output is reduced?

We know that changing $w47$ by a small quantity h will change the input of unit 7 by h * X4 because the contribution from unit 4 to the input of unit 7 will change from w47 * X4 to (w47 + h) * X4. We also know that the coefficient of response of the output of unit 7 with respect to changes in its input is:

$$OI\ (7) = X7 * (1 − X7)$$

So the change in $w47$ leads to the output of unit 7 changing by h * X4 * OI(7).

Finally we know that the coefficient of response of the halfsum of squares of errors with respect to changes in the output of unit 7 is (X7 − r7). So the change of h in $w47$ leads to a change in the target of:

$$h * X4 * OI(7) * (X7 − r7)$$

That is, the coefficient of response of the target with respect to changes in $w47$ is:

$$X4 * OI(7) * (X7 - r7)$$

Let's call this $X4 * CR(7)$, meaning the coefficient of response of the target quantity with respect to changes in the input of unit 7. According to the gradient descent technique, we should change $w47$ by some proportion of this, increasing $w47$ if the output $X7$ is too high, or decreasing it if it is too low.

By a similar argument, we can see that the weights leading into the output layer, namely $w48$, $w57$, $w58$, $w67$, and $w68$, can be adjusted in proportion to the coefficient of response of the target with respect to changes in these weights. These would be, respectively:

$$X4 * CR(8)$$

$$X5 * CR(7)$$

$$X5 * CR(8)$$

$$X6 * CR(7)$$

$$X6 * CR(8)$$

⇨ Adjustment of weights in layers further back in network

What about the coefficients of response of the target with respect to changes in $w14$, $w15$, $w16$ . . . in the next layer back in the network? Starting the analysis in the same way, we see that if we change the weight $w14$ by a small quantity h, the input to unit 4 will change by $h * X1$.

The resulting change in the output of unit 4 will be

$$h * X1 * X4 * (1 - X4)$$

Or, we can say this is equal to h * X1 * OI(4), using the same notation to let *OI*(4) represent the coefficient of response of the output of unit 7 with respect to changes in its input. Let's designate this *Q*.

Now we see an important difference. As discussed earlier, because this change in output *Q* is fed forward to all of the units in the next layer, i.e., both to unit 7 and unit 8, we have to consider the effects produced on the target quantity through both of these units. We know that as a result of the change of output of *Q* from unit 4, the input of unit 7 will change by w47 * Q, and the input of unit 8 will change by w48 * Q. So, the effect of changing w14 by h is that the target quantity will change by:

➤ The effect propagated through unit 7. This will be Q * w47 * CR(7)

➤ The effect propagated through unit 8. This will be Q * w48 * CR(8)

In other words, the total effect on the target quantity is:

$$Q * (w47 * CR(7) + w48 * CR(8))$$

Because Q is h * X1 * OI(4), we can conclude that the rate at which the error will change when changes are made in *w*14 is:

$$X1 * OI(4) * (w47 * CR(7) + w48 * CR(8))$$

Now we see why the calculations have to start with calculating CR(7) and CR(8) for the two output units. These are part of the calculations of the response of the target quantity to changes in the next layer back from the output layer.

By the same argument, we can see that the rate at which the target quantity will change when changes are made in *w*15 and *w*16 would be:

$$X1 * OI(5) * (w57 * CR(7) + w58 * CR(8))$$

and

$$X1 * OI(6) * (w67 * CR(7) + w68 * CR(8))$$

If there were more processing layers, say a layer of units a and b that were inserted before the present input layer of units 1, 2, and 3, we could similarly say that $CR(1)$ or the coefficient of response of the target to changes in the input of unit 1 is figured by considering all the effects that propagate forward through unit 1 as:

$$CR(1) = IO(1) * (w14 * CR(4) + w15 * CR(5) + w16 * CR(6))$$

Consequently, if any change is made in the coefficient $wa1$ connecting unit a in the previous layer to node 1, the coefficient of response of the target quantity would be Xa * CR(1).

Similar computations could be made for estimating the effects of changes in coefficients $wa2$, $wa3$, $wb1$, $wb2$, $wb3$, and so on. The program BACKPROP on the disk with this book allows you to experiment with giving pairs of inputs and desired outputs, and it lets you see how the adjustment of weights is made so as to get the correct results.

⇨ Typical applications

As mentioned earlier, applications involving backpropagation are perhaps the most widely used forms of neural networks. To illustrate how such applications are very useful, let's look at some typical applications.

A report in *The Economist* (January 23, 1993) gives a typical example of how a feedforward network can be used. It says that a neural network program was developed at the University of Sussex in England for predicting gold at two sites in the United States. The report says that 36 different measurements of the earth's magnetic field were used.

We saw that the fundamental structure of a problem that can be solved with a neural network has certain components. Let's see how an application like this would fit the fundamental pattern. First we need a list or pattern of input values that are to be fed forward through the network. Here the measurements of the earth's

magnetic field play this role. We also need some desired outputs that provide the "supervision" used for training the network by getting it to adjust the weights.

The report mentions that measurements from sites where drillings had been carried out was used. So information on how much gold was found at the sites constitutes the desired output that was to be used by the network. The report mentioned that when the trained network was used to predict the likelihood of gold at two sites, its predictions of good yield at one site and of negative results at the other were borne out by drillings at these sites. This example shows how in any situation where you can identify the structure of the problem with the fundamental structure of how the network operates, a useful application can be made.

⇨ The NETtalk network

To conclude this chapter, let's look at what is probably the most famous and classic of the applications of these concepts. This is the NETtalk program developed by Sejnowski and Rosenberg.

Let's review the fundamental structure of the network in Fig. 2-6, which is the typical structure of any multilayered feedforward network. It has an input layer that receives the patterns, a hidden layer that is the first processing layer, and an output layer that is the second processing layer. The output layer produces different patterns corresponding to different patterns at the input; i.e., it classifies the input patterns.

The network designed by Sejnowski and Rosenberg had the goal of classifying input corresponding to letters of the English alphabet. The letters were to be classified in terms of the phoneme represented by the letter. The fundamental units used in written English are the letters of the alphabet, plus punctuation marks. But the fundamental units of spoken English are the different sounds or phonemes that combined together constitute the pronunciation of a word. The same letter corresponds to a different sound in a different context. Consider the sounds associated with the letter "a" in the words father, bake, and bat.

Because the phoneme corresponding to a letter varies depending on what other letters precede and follow it, sequences of seven letters from a passage of text were used as the input, and the network was required to identify the fourth or middle letter in the sequence. There were 7 groups of input units, one for each letter, and each group of input units had 29 units in it. For any one letter, one of the 29 units would be activated. There were 29 possibilities: any of the 26 letters of the alphabet, or a comma, or a period or a blank space.

The passages of text were input as follows: first, letters 1 to 7 were input, then 2 to 8, then 3 to 9, and so on. The 7 input groups were like a window across which the input passage was passed. There were 26 output units, and different combinations of these units indicated different phonemes. So this was a "distributed representation." Each output unit did not uniquely indicate a particular phoneme, but each output unit played a role in identifying different phonemes in combination with different subsets of output units.

The middle or hidden layer had 80 units. The output units were further connected to a speech synthesizer so that when the set of output units corresponding to a particular phoneme was turned on, the sound of that phoneme was produced. So, the network's goal was to turn written text into sound. It would "read aloud" from written material.

Training data was necessary for training the network. This was provided by giving 1024 words. As in all backpropagation networks, the weights were adjusted until the sum of squares of errors was minimized. The result was that after training, if the network was fed words from any passage, it would activate the correct subset of output units representing the corresponding phoneme, which in turn would lead to the sound actually being pronounced.

We can see that this is indeed a case of learning from examples. Examples of words are given, the correct pronunciation is given as part of the training data, and the network learns to produce the correct identification of the words in the training data. Then it generalizes to new words by using its weights. Having trained the network using the training data of pairs of seven letter sequences and corresponding phonemes, the network was given input of new

passages, which were again "windowed" across the seven input groups. The results were so impressive that this classic application is often regarded as one that stimulated further work on backpropagation networks.

Once again, it is worth noting that instead of giving explicit rules about what phoneme corresponds to a letter in what context of letters on either side of the target letter, the network is just given training data and uses the backpropagation rule to adjust its weights. Subsequently, other variations of NETtalk were developed, but the underlying principles were essentially the same.

We have given these two examples to indicate how an understanding of the basic principles of a multilayered feedforward network enables you to see how it is applied in specific cases to categorize input patterns. The number of areas in which such applications have been made is really vast. References at the end of this book give details of some books that list numerous applications in diverse areas.

Hopfield networks

ALL artificial neural networks consist fundamentally of interconnected units or artificial neurons. As mentioned in a previous chapter, different ways of interconnecting the ANs lead to different types of networks. In the last chapter, we saw one widely used way of connecting the units: in feedforward layers.

The essence of this pattern of connections is this: In a strictly layered network, the input layer passes the inputs on to the first processing layer, and the units in this layer pass their outputs on to the units in the second processing layer . . . and so on, until the units in the last processing layer, or the output layer, give the output of the network as a whole. If the network is layered, but not strictly layered, the difference is that outputs from units in some layer could go not just to the very next layer, but also to any subsequent layer. In either case, there is no passing back of outputs to any units in earlier layers: hence the name feedforward.

In contrast to this, there is another widely studied pattern of connections known as the *Hopfield net,* which is *recurrent*, not feedforward. Recurrent means that a unit *A* that sends a signal or output to some other unit *B* might receive *B*'s output as input, or it might receive input from some unit *C* to which *B* had sent its output . . . and so on.

Hopfield nets are named in honor of John Hopfield, whose trendsetting work in the field is credited with stimulating the revival of interest and activity in the field of neural networks in the 1980s. Over the years, Hopfield and others have developed some variations of the original Hopfield network. We will start with the important features of the basic Hopfield network as set out in his key paper, "Neural Networks and Physical Systems with Emergent Collective Computational Capabilities," which was published in 1982. We will then consider subsequent developments and applications that have come out of this basic model.

Fundamental features of the Hopfield network

A Hopfield network consists of a number of units that are fully connected. Every unit is connected to every other unit. As in the case of the ANs we have seen previously, there is a weight associated with each of the inputs that every unit receives from every other unit. Each unit computes the weighted sum of its inputs to generate a net input. Moreover, in the Hopfield design, the weights are symmetrical. The weight *tij* connecting unit *i* and unit *j* is equal to the weight *tji* connecting unit *j* and unit *i*. (See Fig. 3-1.)

Figure 3-1

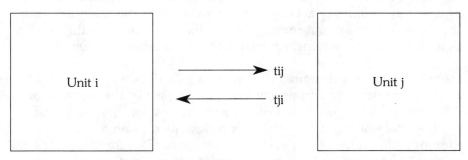

Symmetrical weights in the Hopfield net. tij = tji.

Each of the units uses the hard threshold function of a McCulloch-Pitts neuron to produce an output that is sent to all other units. If the net input is greater than or equal to a threshold T, an output of 1 is sent. Otherwise, an output of 0 is sent. As we saw in the last chapter, a threshold of T can always be treated as equivalent to a weight $w0 = -T$ attached to a constant bias input of 1, with the threshold then being 0.

In a layered network we speak of the network receiving a pattern of inputs at the input layer and producing a pattern of outputs at the final layer. We consider the operation of a Hopfield network in a different way. Each unit in the network could at any point in time be in one of two states that could be described as 0 and 1, or as "not

firing" or "firing." We start by considering the starting state of the network, which can be described by a list of the states of all the units. For instance, if there are 8 units and the first, fourth, and sixth units are in the state 1, and the others are in the state 0, we could say that the initial state of the network is 1 0 0 1 0 1 0 0. We consider this whole pattern as the input to the network.

Because every unit is interacting with every other unit, it is necessary to clearly specify the time sequence of events in a Hopfield network: when does each of the units evaluate its inputs and update itself using its transfer function, thereby changing the input it supplies to all the other units? Hopfield postulated that each unit evaluates its inputs randomly in time, but with a certain average rate of how many times per second or minute it does such updating of itself. Because the time at which each unit updates itself is independent of the times at which the other units carry out their updating, the functioning of the units is described as being unsynchronized with one another, or *asynchronous*.

Hopfield originally designed the network as a device that would retrieve or complete certain patterns if only part of the pattern, or even a slightly distorted part of the pattern, was given to it as the starting state or input pattern. This is described as an *associative memory*: the network will associate the incomplete input with the full pattern it has "learned" or stored, and it will retrieve this. The term CAM or *content addressable memory* is also used in this context.

However, some writers distinguish between the two concepts as follows: A content addressable memory will retrieve one of the patterns it has stored by searching for it, if it is given the content as input. This is in contrast to computers needing information about the address or location for carrying out a search. On the other hand, an associative memory, as the name suggests, can "associate" even distorted or noisy inputs with information it has stored previously, and it can retrieve the stored pattern that is best approximated by the input. In that sense, the concept of an associative memory is more general than that of a content addressable memory.

Hopfield showed that this can be done by assigning the weights according to the following rule: Suppose we want the network to store various patterns a, b, c . . . where each of the patterns consists

of a list of values for units 1, 2, . . . etc. Let's denote pattern a by the list of values:

$$a\_X1 \quad a\_X2 \quad a\_X3$$

. . . and similarly the pattern b by:

$$b\_X1 \quad b\_X2 \quad b\_X3$$

. . . and so on.

The weight tij = tji, connecting any two units i and j both ways should be set equal to the sum:

$$(2 * a\_Xi - 1) * (2 * a\_Xj - 1) +$$

$$(2 * b\_Xi - 1) * (2 * b\_Xj - 1) + . . .$$

. . . i.e., as the sum of the products derived from the values of Xi and Xj for all of the patterns a, b, c . . .

Subsequently, other workers in the field have pointed out that this is equivalent to treating the outputs of the units as having two values, +1 and −1, as follows:

$$\text{When } Xi = 1, \text{ then } 2 * Xi - 1 = 1$$

$$\text{When } Xi = 0, \text{ then } 2 * Xi - 1 = -1$$

So, we can say that we have units with two possible values of output $Yi = 1$ and $Yi = -1$, where $Yi = 2 * Xi - 1$.

For certain analyses, it is convenient to regard a Hopfield net as having units with 1 and 0 outputs or states, and for other purposes as having −1 and 1. In the rest of this chapter we will use these because they are equivalent. However, when changing from considering the net as having inputs of 1 and −1 to having inputs of 1 and 0, an adjustment of the threshold or bias is necessary. We can see this by considering the firing rule for any neuron j. In terms of Y or 1, −1 inputs, the rule is:

$$t1j * Y1 + t2j * Y2 + ... \quad >= 0$$

because Yi = 2 * Xi −1 when the inputs are expressed as X or 1, 0 inputs, the firing rule can be written as:

$$t1j * (2X1 - 1) + t2j * (2X2 - 1) + \ldots >= 0$$

or

$$2 * (t1j * X1 + t2j * X2 + \ldots) >= t1j + t2j + \ldots$$

or

$$t1j * X1 + t2j * X2 + \ldots >= 0.5 * (t1j + t2j + \ldots)$$

In other words, when expressed in terms of Xs, the threshold should be set at 0.5 * (t1j + t2j + . . .) or, as we saw before, a bias of this size should be used in addition to the bias used when expressing the inputs in terms of Ys.

Treating inputs as +1 and −1 simplifies writing the formulas. We can now write, for instance, the weight t37 = t73 as:

$$a\_Y3 * a\_Y7 + b\_Y3 * b\_Y7 + c\_Y3 * cY7$$

. . . and so on. The units do not feed their own current output back to themselves directly, so t11 = t22 = t33 = 0.

The first important result that Hopfield proved was that: in general, when we start the network off with some input pattern, we expect the pattern to keep changing as one unit updates itself, then sends a revised output to the other units and causes a change in the output of some of them when they update themselves . . . However, if the starting state is one of the patterns a, b, c . . . which was used to calculate the weights assigned, then the pattern will usually not change. It will remain persistent or stable.

We could describe this by saying that the network has stored in its memory the "prototype" patterns that were used for setting the weights according to the formulas above. When it is presented with one of these prototype patterns, it "recognizes" it by retaining it unchanged in spite of the interactions of the units. However, more detailed analyses made by Hopfield as well as others have shown that for this to work reliably, various prototypes used for calculating the weights should not

be too similar to each other. A network with *N* nodes can be in any one of 2 ** N different states. But in practice, it can store only about 0.15 * N arbitrarily chosen patterns—much less than 2 ** N.

The property of the network being able to recognize the prototype patterns used to train it is not very important by itself. But it is the starting point of the analysis that leads to the following very important conclusion: if the network is given a pattern different from one of the prototype patterns, it will try to approximate this to one of the patterns it knows. We can describe this as akin to the way the human memory functions: Given a fuzzy picture, we approximate it to some prototype in our memory and recognize the picture as being a fuzzy picture of a friend, or of the Lincoln Memorial or whatever. The detailed analysis of how the network makes this kind of recognition of a "fuzzy" starting input is discussed later in this chapter in the section relating to the "energy" of Hopfield networks. This valuable characteristic of Hopfield networks is also described as the ability to filter out "noise" or distortion in the starting pattern or input pattern.

Before we go on to a discussion of further aspects of the Hopfield network, it would be useful for you to try out the program HOPONE.EXE on the disk. This program allows you to do the following:

➤ Give some three prototype patterns for the network to use for setting its weights. For example, you might try using:

$$1 \ \ 1 \ 0 \ 0 \ \ 0 \ 1 \ 0 \ 1$$

$$0 \ \ 0 \ 1 \ 0 \ \ 0 \ 0 \ 1 \ 1$$

and $\quad 1 \ \ 0 \ 0 \ 0 \ \ 0 \ 1 \ 0 \ 0$

➤ You can then give the program one of these as the input, and you will see that it is "recognized" and kept unchanged through successive updates.

➤ You can give it a pattern slightly different from one of the prototypes, say $1 \ 1 \ 0 \ 0 \ 1 \ 1 \ 0 \ 1$, which is almost the same as the first prototype pattern, but it differs in one of the elements. You will be able to verify that the network approximates this as being close to the first prototype and stabilizes on the first pattern.

 # Energy of a Hopfield network

In his analysis of how these networks function, Hopfield introduced an important concept called the *energy of the network* at any particular point of time. If the state of the network is given by the current values $Y1$, $Y2$, $Y3$ . . . of the output of each of the nodes, where the Ys, as before, are either +1 or −1, then the energy of the network is defined as −0.5 times the following sum S:

$S = Y1 * ($ $t12 * Y2 + t13 * Y3 + t14 * Y4 + ...)$

$+$

$Y2 * (t21 * Y1 +$ $t23 * Y3 + t24 * Y4 + ...) +$

$Y3 * (t31 * Y1 + t32 * Y2 +$ $t34 * Y4 + ...) +$

. . . . .

which we can also write as:

$S = Y1 *$ (net weighted input received by unit 1) +

$Y2 *$ (net weighted input received by unit 2) +

. . . . .

Let's consider what happens to this sum S when some unit, let's say unit 1, randomly evaluates its inputs and uses it transfer function to revise its output. There are four possibilities:

➢ $Y1$ is +1 and the net input is greater than or equal to 0. So $Y1$ is unchanged and continues to be +1. S remains the same, too.

➢ $Y1$ is at −1 and the net input is less than 0. Once again, $Y1$ and S remain unchanged.

➢ $Y1$ is at +1 and the net input is less than 0. Unit 1 will change its output from +1 to −1, i.e., a change of −2. The effect on S is twice −2 * (net input less than 0). The reason it is twice is this: when $Y1$ changes, we see that in the first row, the amount of change will be multiplied by:

$$t12 * Y2 + t13 * Y3 + t14 * Y4 \ldots$$

But looking down the first column we see that in addition, the change in $Y1$ will be multiplied by:

$$t21 * Y2 + t31 * Y3 + t41 * Y4 \ldots$$

because of the symmetric connections of the Hopfield network, i.e., because:

$$t21 = t12, t31 = t13 \ldots$$

We see that the total effect is twice the change in $Y1$ * net input to $Y1$. The same argument would apply to changes in $Y2$, $Y3$. So the change in S is positive, i.e., S increases.

> $Y1$ is at -1 and the net input is greater than or equal to 0. So $Y1$ changes from -1 to $+1$, i.e., a change of $+2$. So effect on S is twice $+2$ * (net input $>= 0$), which is either 0 or a positive number. The reason why -0.5 was introduced in the definition of energy should now be clear. 0.5 * twice the change in $Y1$ * net input to $Y1$ allows us to express the change in energy due to a change in any Y as:

> change in energy = − change in Y of any unit * net input
> to that unit, without having to use a multiplicative factor of 2

The important conclusion we can draw from this is that when the state of the network changes, S can either increase or remain the same. It never decreases. The energy of the network, as defined earlier, is $-0.5 * S$, so it follows that the energy of the network either decreases or remains the same, and it never increases at any step in the series of changes of state of the network. As we previously saw, the change in energy = − change in Y * net input to that unit.

This analysis in terms of the energy of the network leads to the conclusion that whatever the starting state of the network, it will reach a "minimum energy" pattern or configuration after a series of steps, and it will remain stable there. Of course, for different starting patterns, it would settle down on different minima. As we saw earlier,

53

the patterns used as prototypes for getting the weights to be used in the network are usually likely to be stable minima, so there is no unique minimum energy state in which the system will always end up.

There are some problems arising from the fact that there are many possible minima. Suppose we are given an input consisting of a string of 0s and 1s that is not the same as any of the prototypes. Suppose further that one of the prototypes is different from the input in only one of the elements of the string, and the other is different in two elements. This is described by saying that the first prototype is "closer" to the input. Closeness or distance measured by the number of characters in which there is a difference between two strings of 0s and 1s is called the *Hamming distance*.

It is best for the network to find the prototype for which the Hamming distance is least. But this will not always happen. It might find the minimum corresponding to the prototype with a Hamming distance of 2 rather than the one with a Hamming distance of 1. This problem is also described by saying that the net might go to a "local minimum" of energy, i.e., the one that it reaches first, and stay there, even though there is a "global" or better minimum that it does not reach because it does not change any more after reaching the local minimum. We will see in the chapter on Boltzmann machines (chapter 4) that models have been developed to destabilize the system from the local minimum and get it to try to find the global minimum.

The term "energy" was used by Hopfield because of some analogies between the nature of the function he used for networks and the concept of energy in statistical physics. These analogies were helpful in further theoretical analyses of the functioning of neural networks because the theories developed in physics could be applied with appropriate modifications. This is also the reason why it was defined so that the change in energy was negative of the change in Y * net input, which would always be nonnegative so that the standard results regarding a quantity that is minimized could be conveniently used. However, for the purposes of this book, the important thing to remember is only that a function can be defined and that the behavior of the network can be explained in terms of the network trying to find minimum points for the value of that function.

⇨ Hopfield nets and optimization problems

The behavior of Hopfield nets can be seen in terms of their trying to minimize an energy function that depends on the weights in the network, and this has led to another major application of such nets. There are a number of decision problems that depend on trying to minimize some value that is related to various variables. Hopfield pointed out that if some way could be found of identifying the outputs of the units with the values of the decision variables in the problem, and of choosing weights so that the energy of the network can be identified with the variable that the decision maker wants to minimize, then the network could be used to find the solution to the problem by minimizing the energy and finding the associated stable values of the outputs of the units in the network.

⇨ The assignment problem

To illustrate this category of applications of the Hopfield network, let's consider the following problem, which is known as the *assignment problem*. The problem situation is as follows: There are four persons, *A*, *B*, *C* and *D*, each of whom is capable of completing any of four different tasks, *P*, *Q*, *R*, and *S*. However, the time each would take for a particular task is different.

This information can be represented as shown in Table 3-1. Reading down the column for any particular job, for instance, job *P*, the different numbers $m11$, $m21$, $m31$, and $m41$ show the different times that *A*, *B*, *C*, and *D* would take to complete the job, and similarly for the other columns. The goal or objective is to assign one job to one person in such a way that the total time spent by all four together is a minimum.

Table 3-1

Time Required for Task Completion

	P	Q	R	S
A	$m11$	$m12$	$m13$	$m14$
B	$m21$	$m22$	$m23$	$m24$
C	$m31$	$m32$	$m33$	$m34$
D	$m41$	$m42$	$m43$	$m44$

With four persons and four jobs, we can see that because A can be given any one of the four jobs, B can be given any of the other three, and C can be given any of the remaining two, leaving the last job for D, there are 4 * 3 * 2 * 1 (or in the standard notation, 4!, read as 4 factorial) i.e., 24 different ways of assigning the jobs. You could compute the total time for each of these 24 possibilities and find the one involving least total time. But the number of possibilities to be examined increases rapidly: for 5 persons and jobs, 5! is 120, for 6, 6 factorial is 720 . . . and so on.

Efficient methods for solving the problem without examining all the possibilities have been developed. However, this is a type of problem that illustrates how a Hopfield net could be used for solving the problem, provided the total time to be minimized could be identified with the energy function of a net, and provided the on/off states of the units could be identified with the yes/no decision of either assigning or not assigning a particular job to a particular person.

We can see that there are 16 such decisions involved in the previous example because for each job there are 4 decisions on assigning or not assigning that job to each of the four persons. If we set up a Hopfield net in a four-by-four array, we can let the first row represent the decisions on whether or not the first person is given each of the jobs. For example, the state 0 1 0 0 of the first row of units would represent the decision that person A is given the second job Q and not any of the others.

Clearly, something has to be built into the process to ensure that each person gets only one job, i.e., in each row there must be exactly one 1 and three 0s. Again, it is necessary to ensure that each job

goes only to one person, so there must be exactly one 1 and three 0s in each column. The energy function has to be set up to ensure this. Further, the energy function should be such that minimizing the function leads to minimizing the total time spent by all four persons.

All of these requirements could be set up by the following process: Let's call the outputs of the units as $y11$, $y12$ . . . to denote their row and column position (or what comes to the same thing) with the first index showing the person it relates to, and the second index showing the job it relates to. To ensure that the first person gets only one job, we need to put into the energy function the following:

$$y11 * (y12 + y13 + y14) + y12 * (y13 + y14) + y13 * y14$$

We can see that if only one of these is one, i.e., only if the first person gets exactly one job, will this expression be 0. Otherwise, it will be positive. So if we put this, and similar expressions for all the persons, into the energy function, minimizing the energy function will push it to solutions where more than one 1 in any row is avoided.

By the same line of reasoning, to ensure that the first job does not go to more than one person, we need an expression:

$$y11 * (y21 + y31 + y41) + y21 * (y31 + y41) + y31 * y41$$

This will be positive if there is more than one 1 in the first column. Otherwise, it will be 0. Similar expressions will also be needed for the other jobs.

It is also necessary to ensure that the jobs do get assigned. There must be a 1 in the column for each job, but it must be distributed according to the requirements just discussed. This can be taken care of by putting into the cost function:

$$(y11 + y21 + y31 + y41 - 1) ** 2$$

This will be 0 only if the job does get assigned to someone. It will be positive otherwise. Similarly, we can provide for the other jobs to get allocated as well.

The requirements just discussed will ensure that the solution is a viable one. But the ultimate goal is to select from the viable solutions the one that minimizes the total time. To ensure this, we need to relate the weights for the network to the data on times taken by each person. We need to include the following terms in the energy function we are minimizing:

$$m11 * y11 + m12 * y12 + m13 * y13 + m14 * y14$$

$$+ m21 * y21 . . . . .$$

$$. . . . .$$

$$. . . . . + m44 * y44$$

The program HOPTWO.EXE on the disk asks the user to give the values of $m11$, $m12$, etc. On the basis of the considerations regarding the energy function, the program calculates the weights $t12$, $t13$, etc., that should be used, and then shows how to move to the optimal solution. Because of the nature of the energy function, it is necessary also to use the "biasing input" of $y0$ with a constant value of 1. The program also calculates the thresholds or, equivalently, the weights $-t01$, $-t02$, etc.

Further developments

As mentioned earlier, the Hopfield net is credited with generating a revival of the field of neural networks. A vast amount of further developments have taken place using the basic network as the starting point. In particular, it is worth mentioning two aspects:

➤ Hopfield extended his analysis to show that the important properties of the net as an associative memory, etc., would still be there if the ANs were to produce continuous outputs, as when using the sigmoid transfer function instead of just two-valued (0/1 or −1/1) outputs. The title of his paper makes it clear: neurons with graded response have computational properties like those of two-state neurons.

➤ The basic model, as previously explained, has neurons that update themselves asynchronously. Alternative models have

been developed where the neurons all update themselves at specified points in time, or where they continuously keep updating themselves.

In the next chapter, we will see an extension of the Hopfield net that is designed to handle the problem of local minima mentioned in this chapter.

Boltzmann machines

I N the last chapter, we saw that a Hopfield network is a fully connected network that is used for two different kinds of tasks:

➤ It functions as an associative memory that stores prototype patterns and outputs the appropriate pattern even if it is given incomplete input. It does this by retrieving the prototype that is closest to the input.

➤ It can be used to solve problems that can be expressed in terms of minimizing some function of a number of variables. It does this if we can "map" the problem on the network by identifying the variables with the units of the network and setting the weights so as to reflect the requirements of the problem to be solved. We saw how this is done in the example of the assignment problem.

In both of these types of problems, Hopfield showed that the operation of the network can be viewed in terms of its minimizing an "energy" function, which is a function of the values of the outputs of the units and of the weights connecting them. However, in both of these types of applications, Hopfield nets turned out to have a certain limitation. We will discuss this limitation in detail and then go on to see how an alternative design has been developed to overcome the problem.

Let's say we have a Hopfield network with eight units. We defined the state of the network as given by the string of values of the units. Because each unit can have a value of +1 or −1 (or equivalently, 1 or 0), there are in total 2 raised to the power 8 possible states of the network, and we can, knowing the interconnecting weights, calculate the value of the energy for each state of the network. Suppose we draw a graph as in Fig. 4-1. It shows the highest energy state as state 1 and the lowest energy state as state 256.

We saw that the behavior of the network is such that it is never possible to make a transition from a state with a certain energy level to any state with a higher energy level. If it were the case that when the network is in a certain state, it can always make a transition to one or more states with lower energy level, then we can be sure that ultimately the network would end up in the lowest energy level state, state 256, or the *global minimum state*, as it is called.

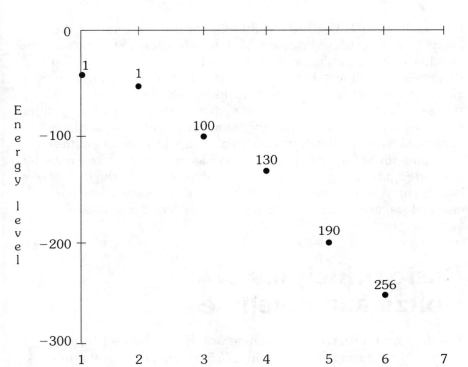

Figure 4-1

Energy levels. The labels on data points show the state number. The lower the number, the higher the energy.

Unfortunately, this is not so. There are some states from which the system cannot transit to any lower energy state (nor, of course, to any higher energy level state). Such states are called *local minima*, meaning that when the network has reached that locality, say by transiting from some higher energy state, there is no other minimum it can go to from there. The fact that the energy levels of Hopfield nets have local minima causes problems in both types of applications. In the case of associative memory, starting from some incomplete data, the network might get trapped in a local minimum representing a prototype other than the one to which the input is really closest. In problems involving optimization of a cost function, clearly we do want the global minimum, and so a local minimum would be a less than completely satisfactory solution.

The type of network known as a *Boltzmann machine* attempts to solve the problem as follows: Suppose the network has gotten

trapped in state 100, which might be a local minimum. But there might be a transition from state 120, which will lead through a series of other transitions ultimately to the global minimum state. The Boltzmann machine is based on the principle of modifying the Hopfield net's absolute ban on transition to higher energy level states. This modification gives the system a better chance of getting out of local minima and following alternative paths to the global minimum. The modification also involves application of another technique for solving minimization problems, which is known as the *simulated annealing* technique. We will look now at the details of a Boltzmann machine and how the transitions to states of higher energy level are regulated. We will also see how the simulated annealing method is used.

Basic principles of Boltzmann machines

The design of a Boltzmann machine or network was set forth by Ackley, Hinton, and Sejnowski in 1985 in a paper with the title "A Learning Algorithm for Boltzmann Machines." The design was subsequently developed in other articles (see the Bibliography). They described it as consisting of units that could be either on or off and linked to each other by symmetric weights. They used 1 and 0 to represent the two possible states of each unit, but as we saw earlier, this is equivalent to using +1 and −1 as the two states. They also mentioned that because of these features, it is similar to or related to the basic Hopfield network, and each state of the network, as described by the collection of on-off states of each of the units, could be identified with a single number called the "energy." However, their design differed from the Hopfield network in terms of the features described in the following.

Probabilistic update rule

The first important difference is that the Boltzmann machine can change from a lower energy state to a higher energy state. As

previously discussed, it is a defining characteristic of the Hopfield network that energy cannot increase in any change of state. This is what leads to the problem that the system might become stable in a local minimum because there is no path from that minimum to a lower minimum.

The Boltzmann machine design regulates transitions to states of higher energy level as follows: Suppose it is the turn of some unit i, which has been randomly selected, to evaluate its input and decide on what its next state should be. We know that according to the rules of the Hopfield network, the next state of the unit would be +1 if the net input is greater than or equal to 0, and the next state of the unit would be −1 if the net input is less than 0. We saw that this is equivalent to saying that the energy will never increase. In place of this rule, the Boltzmann machine uses a probabilistic rule: Irrespective of the current state of the unit, the next state of the unit will be:

1 or ON with a PROBABILITY = $p = 1/(1 + EXP(-G/T))$

0 or OFF with a PROBABILITY = $1-p$

In this expression for the probability, *EXP* is the standard mathematical function, the exponential function, which we have already seen in connection with the sigmoid function used in feedforward networks. T is a positive number that, as we will see shortly, can be adjusted to have different values at different stages of the process of stabilization of the network. G is the *energy gap*, or the energy of the system if the unit is off, minus the energy of the system if the unit is on. So, if the energy gap G is a positive number, it means that the energy of the system is higher if the unit is 0. So, for minimizing energy, having the unit at 1 is preferable. On the other hand, if the energy gap G is a negative number, it means that having the unit at 0 is the preferable state.

What are the implications of this rule that irrespective of the current state there are probabilities that the unit could be either 1 or 0 at the next stage? Suppose the current state of the unit, either 0 or 1, is the state of lower energy in relation to the other state. Because of the probabilistic rule, it might either remain in its current state, with the energy of the network unchanged, or it

might switch to the other state that involves higher energy. This is in contrast with a Hopfield net, where the unit would never switch in such a situation.

On the other hand, suppose the current state of the unit, either 0 or 1, is the one of higher energy in terms of the energy gap. The probabilistic rule says the unit might switch, which leads to lower energy, or it might remain unchanged, without any change in energy. Again we can see the contrast with the Hopfield network, where the unit would always switch in such circumstances. We see therefore that the possibilities of going to higher energy levels arise because of the probabilistic rule.

The preceding expression for the probability p that the unit would be on at the next stage, and the probability $(1 - p)$ that it would be off can be rewritten in the form:

$$p/(1 - p) = \exp(G/T)$$

$p/(1 - p)$ are what we call the odds that it will be on, or the ratio of the probabilities of the unit being on or off.

From the form of the expression, we can see the following: Let's say the energy gap is 0, meaning the total energy of the network is the same whether this unit is on or off. $\exp(0)$ is 1. The odds are 1 to 1 whether the unit will be on or off. This is reasonable because if the energy associated with the two states are the same, there is no reason for one of the states to have higher odds.

Suppose the energy gap G is negative, meaning the energy is higher with the unit on than with the unit off. For a given value of T, the larger the magnitude of this negative number, the smaller the odds that the unit will switch to the higher energy state. This is because *exp* of a negative number is always less than one, and also it is smaller when the magnitude or size of the negative number is bigger. So, the higher the energy level of on compared to off, the less the probability of making the jump. So, only very rarely will the system go to states that increase the energy by a large amount. So the energy can go up, but with more probability of going up a little, and very little probability of going up by a lot.

On the other hand, suppose the energy gap G is a positive number, meaning the energy level will be less with the unit ON. The exponential of any positive number is greater than 1, so the odds are in favor of going to lower energy states.

For a given negative energy gap, say −1, the larger the T is, the smaller is −1/T, and the higher the value of exp(− 1/T). So, if T is very large, the probability of going up in energy by a certain amount is higher than if T is small. In other words, a low value of T inhibits jumps to higher levels of energy. As T becomes closer and closer to 0, the probability of jumping up by even a small amount is very small. One can think of a Hopfield net as a Boltzmann net with $T = 0$, for in that case the probability is 0 of any jump to a higher energy level.

The Boltzmann machine uses high values of T in the earlier stages of evolution of the network and gradually reduces the value of T. Intuitively, the rationale for this is as follows: To start with, one would like the network to have relatively more freedom to explore alternative paths towards the global minimum by making jumps to higher energy level states. But after this has gone on a bit, it is likely that the system would be in one of the states of relatively lower energy, and it would be wasteful to let it go back to very high levels and start all over again.

The value of T, which controls the process as previously described, is called the *temperature*. The reason for this, as well as the reason for calling this design a Boltzmann machine, is that the expression for the probability as previously given was developed by the eminent physicist Ludwig Boltzmann in connection with studies of heat and thermodynamics. In that field, of course, temperature was the temperature of the bodies involved and the energy was the thermal energy of the molecules in the bodies. Boltzmann had shown that eventually the transitions would lead to a "thermal equilibrium" in which the probabilities of the system being in states A and B would be given by:

$$\text{Prob}(A) / \text{Prob}(B) = \text{EXP}((\,E(B) - E(A))/T)$$

where $E(A)$ and $E(B)$ are the energies of the two states. $E(B) - E(A)$ is the energy gap. The distribution of probabilities of states according to this rule is referred to as a Boltzmann distribution.

Using a low value for T, the probability of a low energy state is relatively much higher, but it would take much longer to stabilize. With a high T, the relative probabilities of high and low energy states are more nearly equal. The designers of the Boltzmann network pointed out that a good tradeoff would be to start with a higher "temperature" and then reduce the value of T or "cool" the system.

A similar technique using the Boltzmann distribution had been adopted by Kirkpatrick and others for solving minimization problems. They had called the method "simulated annealing" because of the analogy with the physical process of annealing certain metals by first heating them to a high temperature and then cooling them slowly. Ackley, Hinton, and Sejnowski also pointed out in their paper that this probability expression is also related to the measures of information developed by Claude Shannon in his path-breaking communication theory or information theory.

Because of the probabilistic behavior of the units, the final state reached by the network is not static. The units will still be making transitions according to the probabilities, but they would be found most of the time in the global minimum state, making occasional transitions to higher levels of energy.

⇨ Hidden units

A second very important feature that distinguishes the Boltzmann machine from the Hopfield net is the existence of hidden units. In a Hopfield net, the starting state is fed to the whole collection of units. The network evolves from state to state through successive updates and ends up with the final state. In other words, the whole collection of units constitutes a layer of input units at the start and is also the output units at the end. There is nothing analogous to the hidden units in multilayer feedforward networks.

In the Boltzmann machine, the designers introduced other units in addition to the units that receive the input (or set at a starting state) and finally provide the output or result. They argued that one of the problems with a Hopfield network is that when it is used to store prototype patterns and retrieve them on the basis of incomplete

input, certain restrictions operate if the network is to operate reliably. Broadly speaking, the different patterns to be stored should be as distinct from each other as possible. If they are so different from each other that (if we consider them as vectors of 0 and 1) no two of them have a 1 in the same place, then all the prototypes would be stored and retrieved accurately.

But in practice the prototypes to be stored would not satisfy this requirement, and in such circumstances, studies have shown that a Hopfield network with N units can reliably store about 15% of N prototypes. For example, with a 100-unit network, you can store about 15 prototypes. The problem can be illustrated by looking at a network with 3 units. Suppose we want it to store the four patterns:

$$0 \quad 0 \quad 0$$

$$1 \quad 0 \quad 1$$

$$0 \quad 1 \quad 1$$

$$1 \quad 1 \quad 0$$

In the final state we can see that this requires that the inputs to the third unit should be as follows: The second and third patterns require that the weights should be such that the weighted input from either the first or second unit by itself should be enough to keep the third unit on. But if that is so, then in the fourth pattern when both the units are on, the third unit will be on too. We want the third unit to be on when one or the other of the two units is on, but not when neither or both or on. In other words, what we have is really the same exclusive OR problem, which, as we saw when we discussed the perceptron, was insoluble with a single layer of units.

The Boltzmann machine solves problems of this type by introducing hidden units. If a hidden unit h is introduced, we can think of the hidden unit as something that is inactive when neither or one of the first two units is active, but:

➢ Becomes active when both the first units are active.

➢ Then turns off unit three by using a negative weight for the input it gives the third unit.

```
                          h

            0     0     0     0

            1     0     0     0

            0     1     1     0

            1     1     0     1
```

Ackley, Hinton, and Sejnowski showed that with hidden units, a procedure that would work would be as follows: First, the input and output units are *clamped* or kept at the desired values, and the system is allowed to move to equilibrium. To reinforce their association, the weights are then increased between units that are on. This is called the first phase. Then, clamping only the input units, the system is allowed to go to equilibrium. This is the second phase. The units that are on have their weights decreased. The reason for this is the following: Some of the units that are together represent poor associations and should be "discouraged." Others that are on and represent good associations have been "encouraged" in the first phase, so they do not get any net discouragement. This is repeated until the weights are stable. The net result is that the network will learn the patterns and will retrieve them correctly.

To get a concrete idea of how a Boltzmann machine works, you might like to try the program BOLTZ.EXE on the disk. It allows you to see how sometimes there are jumps to levels of higher energy and how adjusting the temperature makes such jumps more likely or less likely. Please see the instructions on using the program, which are given in Part II of the book.

5

Unsupervised learning

CHAPTER 5

O NE of the leading researchers in the field of neural networks, Teuvo Kohonen, points out that the design or architecture of neural networks can be roughly divided into three categories:

➤ Feedforward networks, which transform patterns of input signals into patterns of output signals. We saw the basic example of this in the chapter on backpropagation (chapter 2). We give the network an input pattern and a matching output pattern or desired response. We also provide a learning rule that the network should use to adjust the weights to get a pattern of output as close as possible to the desired response. (Closeness is measured by the sum of squares of the differences between the desired and actual output at each of the output nodes.) This is called a form of *supervised learning* because the network learns or minimizes the sum of squares of errors using the desired outputs as guidance.

➤ Feedback networks. Kohonen cites the Hopfield network as the standard example of a feedback network. We have seen how in such a network the input sets up an "initial state" of all the units in the network. The units then interact with one another, and the output from any unit goes to all the other units, which process it and in turn send back their output or *feed it back* to the first unit. Ultimately all the units stabilize, and this collection of stable states is the final state or output of the network.

➤ The third category, which we will look at in this chapter, operates in a different way. This category of networks is called by various names, and one of the names is *competitive learning* network. As we examine the working of this type of network, the reason for the name will become clear. We will then consider alternative ways of looking at the operation of such networks and the alternative names that have been given to them.

Basics of competitive learning

The fundamental organization of a competitive learning network of the Kohonen pattern is as follows: Let's say there are a number of

input nodes, which receive inputs of $X1$, $X2$, $X3$ . . . . The values are not restricted to 0 and 1 and can be any real number, positive or negative. We have a Kohonen layer of units, each of which is connected to each of the inputs. Let's say there are 100 such units. These are arranged in a square of 10 by 10, and we can think of them as units 1 to 10 in the first row, 11 to 20 in the second row, and so on, as shown in Fig. 5-1.

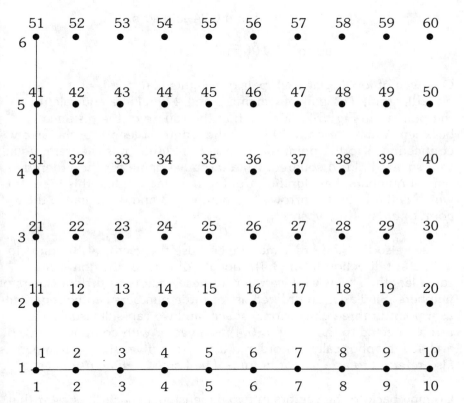

Figure 5-1

The Kohonen layer. The diagram shows 6 of the 10 layers of 10 units each.

The weights associated with the inputs are different for each of the units in the output layer. Suppose we consider the simple case of two inputs, $X1$ and $X2$. The first unit in the output layer would have a pair of weights that we can call $w11$ and $w21$, with the double index 11 signifying the weights connecting input 1 to output 1. Similarly,

the index 21 signifies the weight connecting input 2 to output 1. Using the same notation, the output units 2, 3, 4 . . . would have the weights associated with them as:

w12 and w22

w13 and w23

w14 and w24 and so on

up to w1,100 and w2,100

One way of looking at each pair of weights is to think of it as a point on a diagram. The pair of weights 3 and 4 would be equivalent to the point A in Fig. 5-2. We see that the square of the distance between A and the point (0,0), or the length of length of the arrow connecting A to the point (0,0) is, by the Pythagoras theorem, equal to 3 squared plus 4 squared. An alternative name for the ordered pair of numbers that signifies a point in a diagram like this is *vector*, which is the Latin for arrow. The numbers 3 and 4 are called the *components* of the vector.

We see also that the order matters because the vector (4,3) points in a different direction from (3,4), though, of course, they have the same length. This is why we refer to these vectors as *ordered* pairs of numbers. Similarly, an ordered list of three numbers can be regarded as a point in three-dimensional space, and we can still visualize an arrow directed to the point (3,6,4) as a vector with components 3, 6, and 4. Metaphorically, an ordered list of four, five, six . . . numbers is also referred to as a vector in four-, five-, six- . . . dimensional space.

Coming back to the vectors in two-dimensional space, it is clear that if we think in terms of "travelling" along the vector, starting from 0,0 and going towards 3,4, the x and y coordinates have the same ratio 3 to 4 for all points on the line. If we reduce 3 and by the same proportion say half, to 1.5 and 2, the direction from 0 0 to the new point B, which is (1.5,2), remains the same. Similarly, if we increase both components by the same proportion, say triple them, then the vector pointing to (9,12) has the same direction, too.

Figure 5-2

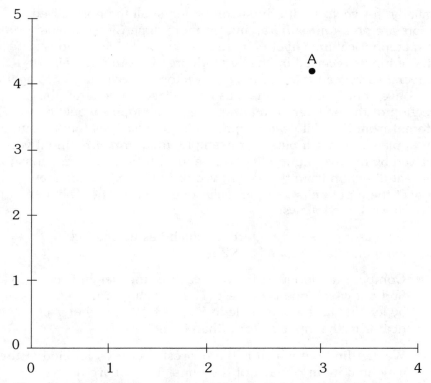

The pair of weights 3 and 4 would be equivalent to the point A.

It is convenient, though not essential, to choose the weights so that the sum of squares of the weights equals 1. When the weights are chosen this way, they are said to be *normalized*. In general, the vector (a,b) will have length equal to the square root of (a ** 2 PLUS b ** 2), so to normalize any vector so as to make the length 1, we need to divide each of the components by this length.

We can normalize the vector (3,4) by dividing each of the components by the square root of 3 ** 2 plus 4 ** 2. We get 0.6 and 0.8, and the sum of these squares is 1. We can think of all normalized vectors as being at distance 1 from (0,0), but in different directions. This is described by saying that all of them are on the *unit circle*. So, the different output units have weight vectors that point in different directions in the unit circle.

Similarly, for vectors with three components, all the normalized vectors are on a *unit sphere*, and for more dimensions, they are on the metaphorical *unit hypersphere* of 4, 5, 6 . . . dimensions. The pairs of inputs received by the network are also ordered pairs of numbers, so we can think of them as vectors as well, and once again it is convenient to think of them as normalized. In general, the direction of the unit vector that represents the inputs would be different from the unit vector representing the weights that an output unit applies to these inputs. For example, the normalized input vector received by the two input units may be (0.2, 0.98). This responds to a different direction from the weight vector (0.6, 0.8), which may connect the input units to a particular output unit. The Kohonen network works as follows:

> Give as input some pattern a, which has normalized components a_X1 and a_X2.

> Compare the input vector with each of the weight vectors to find out which one is nearest. The meaning of nearest is clear by looking at the unit circle in Fig. 5-3. We see that vector P is nearer to the input vector a than is vector Q.

> We can find out which is the nearest vector by looking at the weighted input of each of the units. The square of the distance between the points $(X1, X2)$ and $(w11, w21)$ in Fig. 5-3 would be:

$$(X1 - w11) ** 2 + (X2 - w21) ** 2$$

This is because the vertical distance between them is $X1 - w11$, and the horizontal distance is $X2 - w21$, hence the square of the distance between them is, by the Pythagoras theorem, equal to the sum of the squares of the horizontal and vertical distances. This expression simplifies to:

$$(w11 ** 2 + w21 ** 2)$$

$$+ (X1 ** 2 + X2 ** 2)$$

$$- 2 * (w11 * X1 + w21 * X2)$$

Figure 5-3

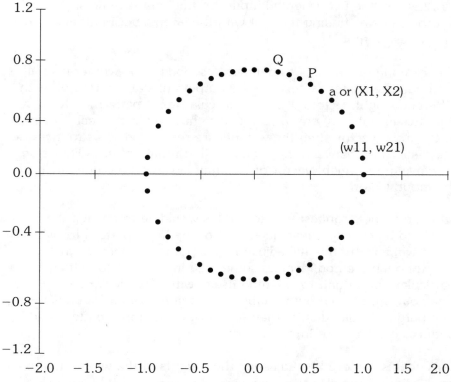

Vectors on a unit circle.

Because we are using both the weight vectors and input vectors in normalized form, the first two terms equal 1 each, and we recognize the last term as the standard form of the net weighted input to the output unit. So we can further simplify the expression for the distance:

$$2 - 2 * \text{net weighted input} =$$

$$2 * (1 - \text{net weighted input})$$

We know that when the input vector and the weight vector are the same, the distance is 0, i.e., the expression (1 – net weighted input) is 0, or the net weighted input is 1. For any other weight vector, the more the distance, the more the value of (1 – net weighted input),

i.e., the less the net weighted input. So finding the nearest vector is just the same as finding the unit with the largest net input and hence the largest output.

The Kohonen method is sometimes described as a "winner-take-all" method. The reason is because the output units are started off with different weight vectors. If for a particular input pattern, a_X1 a_X2, a particular unit, say unit 3, is found to have a weight vector nearest to the input vector, then the weights are readjusted so as to increase the association between that unit and that input pattern. This is done by moving the weight vector of that unit closer on the unit circle to the input vector.

Of course, the strongest way to do this would be to change the weight vector to be exactly the same as that of the input pattern for which it is the winner. But this full adjustment is not made because the goal of the Kohonen method involves something in addition to getting a particular output unit to "identify itself" with a particular input vector. The goal is that each output unit and a *neighborhood* of units near that output should identify themselves with that input pattern and patterns close to that input pattern.

This goal is achieved by adjusting the weights of the winner unit by a proportion of the difference between the current weight vector and the input vector. We can imagine each of the patterns or pairs of numbers as coming from a random selection from a whole set of such pairs, as in Fig. 5-4.

We want the winner to identify itself not just with one pattern but with other patterns close to it because we would like it to figure out that there are three clusters of the data. So, the weights associated with unit 3 are not made exactly the same as that of pattern *a*. They are changed as follows:

$$w13 = w13 + alpha * (a\_X1 - w13)$$

$$w23 = w23 + alpha * (a\_X2 - w23)$$

where alpha is a number between 0 and 1.

Figure 5-4

```
    *******                *******

   ********   ******        *******
'a' is in this cluster    'b' is in this cluster




                      ******* 'c'
```

We can imagine each of the patterns or pairs of numbers as coming from a random selection from a whole set of such pairs.

Secondly, we want the units that are near the winning unit to have the same sensitivity to this cluster of input patterns so a neighborhood of units of the winning units, say the ones not more than two units away from the winning unit, also have their weights adjusted. The weights for the other units are left unchanged. The result of these adjustments is that when another input pair with the same value or from a point close to a is again received, unit 3 and units in its neighborhood would have a competitive advantage in getting large outputs for these input vectors, and they would again have their weights adjusted.

As the process is repeated with a number of input data, unit 3 and units in its neighborhood would end up with a weight pair that is the same as the average of the weight pair of the cluster around point a in Fig. 5-4. Similarly, other units would end up with weight pairs that are the average of the clusters for which, so to speak, they have become the "designated detectors." In other words, after the units have been fed a number of randomly selected samples of input, they sort themselves out so that corresponding to clusters in the data, units set themselves to have weight pairs that indicate that data.

The program KOHONEN.EXE on the disk is designed to give a hands-on view of how the weight pairs, starting at random, arrange themselves to reflect the clusters in the input data. It uses 100 output units, arranged in a 10-by-10 block as previously discussed. Input patterns are selected randomly from a distribution as in Fig. 5-4.

After a number of such samples have been fed to the network, the weights associated with the 100 units align themselves to reflect the fact that there are three clusters around the representative points a, b, and c. This is described by saying that the pattern of weights in the 10-by-10 arrangement of units produces a *feature map* of the patterns of vectors in the various samples that have been fed to the network.

An alternative name for this kind of network is "unsupervised learning," and now we can see why. The network detects by itself the existence of clusters, and it orients its weight pairs to indicate the clusters.

Adaptive resonance network

Another very interesting network is an *adaptive resonance network*, or ART, associated with the names of the leading researchers Gail Carpenter and Stephen Grossberg. It is based on using a layer that is a competitive network of neurons operating on the "winner-take-all" principle, though it involves many further elaborations. ART is the name of a class of networks rather than a single specific pattern. ART1 was the original design, followed by ART2, ART3, and then ARTMAP. We will start by looking at the original ART1, and then we will briefly comment on the further developments.

As mentioned in an earlier chapter, there are two broad categories of researchers in neural networks. Those with an engineering emphasis are primarily interested in designing networks to replicate complex information processing tasks that the brain is capable of, irrespective of whether the networks provide a plausible model for how the human brain works. The other group of workers are interested in the human cognition aspect, and they work with models that are plausible models of the human brain. The work of Carpenter,

Grossberg, and their associates is in the latter category, and some of the terminology used reflects this emphasis. In various writings, Grossberg has pointed out certain aspects of human learning that ART aims to embody:

Human beings learn many things by trial and error and by interacting with the environment without being given explicit rules. Children in particular learn to handle objects and so forth using their experience as a guide. In other words, unsupervised learning is an important facet of human learning and intelligence.

Grossberg has pointed out what he calls the *stability-plasticity dilemma*. This refers to the fact that on the one hand it is necessary to adapt to and learn new things: there is a need for plasticity. On the other hand, this plasticity should not affect or distort things already learned: this is the need for stability. One of the problems with artificial neural networks is that once they have learned to store a set of patterns and retrieve them, if we try to add further patterns for them to learn, it often adversely affects their performance on previously learned patterns. This is sometimes referred to as *catastrophic forgetting*.

We saw, for instance, that in the backpropagation method, the weights are adjusted by using a training set of patterns to minimize the sum of squares of errors of the outputs produced for the whole set. If a new input-output pair is also to be added to the repertoire of the network, the ANN would typically have to be retrained on the expanded set. In other words, the previous learning is not sufficiently stable. What is needed is something analogous to the human ability to acquire new knowledge and adjust old knowledge in the light of the new knowledge. On the other hand, it is necessary that old knowledge should not be too easily modified. Some stability in retaining old knowledge is necessary.

Let's look at the fundamental features of the ART network and see how it handles the stability-plasticity dilemma. The ART network consists of a layer of units that receive 1 or 0 signals as inputs. In terms of the terminology of vectors, we can say that each input is a vector or list of 1s and 0s. We can also think of it as a string or set of positions. In some positions, a bit is on (1), and in other positions it is off (0).

This layer that receives inputs is called the *feature detection* layer of the network, and it is designated F1, as in Fig. 5-5. As we saw when we discussed the Kohonen network, the goal of competitive networks is to classify groups of similar patterns into clusters. We can think of the 0s and 1s as indicating the absence or presence of features that we use for classifying whether some patterns are similar and others are different.

Figure 5-5

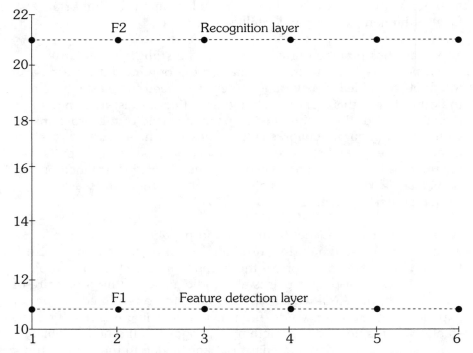

ART network. Every unit i in the recognition layer F2 is connected to every unit j in the feature detection layer F1, with a weight tij.

There is another layer of units, each of which is connected to each of the units in the feature detection layer. As usual, these use a list of weights. This layer is called the *recognition layer* and is designated as F2. Each unit of this layer can be thought of as associated with or identified with a particular vector that is a list of 1s and 0s. Each output unit represents a particular prototype pattern. We will see in a moment where this pattern is stored.

The network transmits patterns both ways, from F1 to F2 and from F2 to F1. We will see later that the network involves a mechanism for deciding when patterns should go from F1 to F2 and when they should go from F2 to F1. Each unit in F2 is connected to each unit in F1 with a weight. This weight vector or list of weights is the prototype with which that unit is identified. In the form of the vector of weights connecting it to the input units, each output unit stores the prototype pattern it is identified with or represents. Because of the ART orientation towards cognitive science that was mentioned earlier, these weights are referred to as *long-term memory* or LTM.

Suppose we have six input units that receive inputs of $X1$, $X2$, $X3$, $X4$, $X5$, and $X6$, where each of the Xs is either a 0 or a 1. These values are referred to as *short-term memory* or STM. Let the weights connecting the input units and the first unit in the recognition layer be: $t11$, $t12$, $t13$, $t14$, $t15$, and $t16$. This is the LTM of unit 1 in the F2 layer. The letter t is used to indicate that these are the weights "top down" for patterns transmitted from the top F2 layer to the bottom F1 layer. As before, a double index like $t14$ indicates it is the weight connecting top unit 1 to bottom unit 4.

The weights $t11$, $t12$ . . . are the weights for transmission of patterns from top to bottom. How are the inputs summed up for transmission to the top? First, a weighted sum is formed of the values of the Xs and of the top-to-bottom weights. For example, for transmitting the input to top unit 1, the weighted sum first formed is:

$$t11 * X1$$

$$+ t12 * X2$$

$$+ t13 * X3$$

$$+ t14 * X4$$

$$+ t15 * X5$$

$$+ t16 * X6$$

Each of the products $t11 * X1$, $t12 * x2$ . . . in this weighted sum would be 0 if either or both of t and X are 0. It would be 1 only if both the t and the X are 1. In other words, the weighted sum

represents the number of positions in which the input vector and the weight vector both have a 1. For example, suppose we have six units, and the input pattern has four 1s and its weighted sum is formed with two different weight vectors:

input	1	1	0	1	0	1
wtvec1	0	1	0	0	0	1
wtvec2	1	1	0	1	0	0

The weighted sum using the weight vector *wtvec*1 is 2, and the weighted sum using *wtvec*2 is 3. These numbers tell us the number of places in which the input pattern and the weight vector both have 1s.

Next, this weighted sum is divided by the total number of 1s in the weight vector plus a small positive number. This will give a number between 0 and 1. To see the purpose of adding a small positive number, let's see what happens if we divide by just the number of 1s in the weight vector.

In the example above, 2/2 will give us 1 and for *wtvec*2, and 3/3 will also give us 1. We can see that what this calculation does: It tells us what proportion of the 1s in the stored prototype match 1s in the input pattern. To put it another way: Each 1 in the weight vector *captures* a 1 in the input pattern when it matches it, and the ratio tells us what fraction of the 1s in the weight vector are *effective* in capturing 1s in the input vector.

But we would like to give a higher score to a prototype that matches more of the 1s in the input pattern. We see that 2/ 2+p will give us 1/ 1+ 0.5 p. On the other hand, 3/ 3+ p will give 1/ 1.0.33p. The latter has a smaller denominator, and so gives a higher value, which is what we want for a vector that matches more of the 1s in the input pattern. However, even with the addition of the small positive number, we can interpret the value we have given as basically telling us what fraction of the 1s in the weight vector capture 1s in the input. We could call it the *capture coefficient*. It tells us how effectively the 1s in the weight vector use the 1s without "wasting" any of them in positions where the input vector has a 0.

We can think of the net input sent to the top layer units in another way. We formed the weighted sum using the top-down weights and then divided them by the total number of 1s in the list, plus a small positive number. Clearly, this is the same as using weights:

$$t11' = t11 \ / \ (\text{sum of 1s} + p) \ ,$$

$$t12' = t12 / (\text{sum of 1s} + p) \ . \ . \ . \ .$$

when forming the weighted sum of $X1$, $X2$ . . . etc. So the weights $t11'$, $t12'$ . . . used for bottom-up transmission are derived from the weights used for top-down transmission, but they are scaled down. They are said to be *normalized*. (Here normalization or scaling down is done in a different way from normalization of vectors that we saw in an earlier part of this chapter.)

For transmission to each of the units in layer F2, a weighted sum is formed in the same way as just discussed. The output unit that has the maximum weighted input is provisionally chosen as the one to which the input pattern is assigned. Why provisionally? The capture coefficient calculated above for provisionally choosing the best output unit tells us how effectively the weight vector or prototype is using its 1s for matching 1s in the input pattern. But another factor has to be considered.

To take an extreme case, let's say we have an input vector with four 1s in it, and we use a weight vector with just one 1 and five 0s. With that 1 matching a 1 in the input, this vector would get a score of $1/1 + p$ or nearly 100% as its capture coefficient because it is using all (1) of its 1s for capturing 1s in the input vector. But suppose there is another weight vector with four 1s in it, of which three are in the same position as 1s in the input vector. Because three of the four 1s in the weight vector match 1s in the input vector, this second vector would get only a score of $3/ (4 + p)$ or about 75%. But clearly it is a closer fit to the input vector because three of the 1s are matched.

To allow for this kind of situation, the ART method uses a further calculation. After selecting the input vector that captures the largest fraction of the 1s in the input vector, a further computation is made: what proportion of the 1s in the input vector have been captured by

the weight vector? The higher this is, the better the weight vector is said to *resonate* with the input pattern. In the previous example, because the vector with just a single 1 captures only one of the four 1s in the input pattern, it has a resonance of only ¼. The other vector has a resonance of ¾. A weight vector with exactly the same pattern as the input vector would of course capture all the 1s in the input pattern and would have a resonance of 1.

We can calculate the resonance by taking the weighted sum of the *t*s and *X*s, as before, which gives us the number of matches of 1s. Dividing this by the number of 1s in the input vector will give us the proportion or fraction of 1s in the input vector that have been matched or captured (just as dividing it by the number of 1s in the weight vector gave us the proportion of 1s in the weight vector that are effective).

Keeping this consideration of resonance in mind, the ART method tests the weight vector that has been selected as capturing the largest fraction of input 1s to see if it passes a test for a minimum amount of resonance. The minimum cutoff for resonance is called the *vigilance factor*. We can see intuitively that using a low value for the vigilance factor means that the input patterns will be grouped into a smaller number of categories or clusters. Even somewhat dissimilar patterns will have enough resonance to be put into the same cluster. On the other hand, using a high vigilance factor will lead to more categories because even a small difference in resonance will mean that the patterns will go into different clusters.

If the provisionally selected weight vector passes the vigilance test, the unit associated with it has its weight adjusted to bring it closer to the input pattern. This is done by deleting from the weight vector any 1s that were not capturing 1s in the input pattern, i.e., were in positions where there were 0s in the input pattern. The result would be: the next time the same input pattern is presented, the capture coefficient would be higher because redundant 1s in the weight vector have been eliminated. We see that this reinforces the identification of that output unit with that pattern.

However, if the resonance is not above the vigilance level, that output unit is rejected as a candidate for assigning that particular

input pattern. The unit with the next highest capture rate for input 1s is tested to see if it passes the vigilance test, and so on. If none of the existing units passes the vigilance test, the input pattern is assigned to a new unit that has so far not had any unit assigned to it. The network is designed to start with all the output units unassigned, and these are assigned as input units are successively presented to the network.

Once the input pattern has been assigned, the process is repeated with all the other input patterns in the training set. Some of the patterns will be assigned to different units. Some will be clustered or grouped with the same unit.

Grossberg, Carpenter, and other workers in the field proved rigorously that a network based on these principles will resolve the stability-plasticity dilemma. Patterns that are "close" to each other, in the sense of being different in only a few positions, would be assigned to the same output unit. The change in weights made when a new pattern is assigned to a unit will not "destabilize" the allocation of a previous pattern to that unit. The groups or clusters assigned to different output units would be significantly different from those in other clusters.

⇨ Architecture of ART

As mentioned earlier, the ART network works by first using the inputs to send a weighted sum to the recognition layer units, using the normalized weights $t11'$, $t12'$, etc. At this stage, transmission from F1 to F2 has to be enabled or allowed, and transmission from F2 to F1 disabled. The unit that receives the maximum weighted input is provisionally selected or turned on. A signal is sent from this "winner" to set all the other output units at 0 so that they cannot send any signal to the F1 layer. Now transmission from F2 to F1 is enabled. The unit that is turned on sends a signal of 1, which is now transmitted top-down to the units in the feature detection layer. The signal of 1, transmitted with the top-down weights $t11$, $t12$ . . . will of course produce the list:

$$1 * t11 \ 1 * t12 \ . . . .$$

at the input units, i.e., it will transmit the stored prototype to the input units. As mentioned earlier, this will be compared with the input vector. Any 1s in the weight vector that are not matched by 1s in the input vector will be deleted, and the modified vector will be resonated back to the recognition layer.

The ART network requires additional units that will enable and disable transmission from F1 to F2 or F2 to F1 at the appropriate stages by sending control signals. Also, when a particular output unit does not pass the vigilance test, it has to be disabled and the search for the best fit has to be made from the remaining output units.

⇨ Further developments

The basic ART1 just described deals with binary signals: 0 or 1. Subsequently, Grossberg and Carpenter developed a series of models involving more theoretical complexity, and we will just briefly mention the highlights. ART2 was designed to handle signals that could be any real number, not just 0 or 1. ART3 introduced a further level of sophistication by allowing for signals that could vary continuously. ARTMAP is the latest development made by Carpenter and Grossberg. In a variation of the purely unsupervised learning in the previous models, ARTMAP introduces supervision into the learning process.

6

Etc.

T HE study and development of neural computing has expanded vastly in the last decade. So immense is the progress that no single book can cover the field comprehensively. A look at the Proceedings of the World Congress on Neural Networks organized by the International Neural Network Society in July 1993 gives a good indication of the prodigious amount of work going on in this field. Two of the volumes are more than 600 pages each, and the other two are more than 800 pages each.

The papers cover a vast variety of applications, as well as theoretical developments in all aspects of neural networks. The papers also show that the largest amount of work on neural computing so far has been done by simulating neural networks on conventional computers. This has led to deeper understanding and development of how neural networks operate. But obviously, the inherent advantage of the parallelism of such computers would be fully exploited if they could be implemented in hardware. This is one of the major directions in which current progress is being made. Of particular interest are the *optical neural networks* that are being developed. Instead of using electronic transmission of signals, these computers use optical signals, with the associated advantages of speed.

Core concepts

Underlying all these developments, there is a central body of concepts that:

> ➤ Provides the foundation of the field.

> ➤ Equips people to pursue further whichever aspects of the field are of interest and relevance to them.

This book has tried to focus on conveying a sound understanding of these core concepts, with the programs on disk as a supplementary learning and reinforcement device. The following is a summary and capsule review of these core ideas.

The most central concept is that of parallel processing using simple processing units instead of a complex CPU. In this context, there is a

distinction between the kind of parallelism we have considered and a different kind of parallelism known as *massively parallel computing*. The latter relies on using a large number of complex CPUs, dividing up a task between these CPUs, and then coordinating them. Massively parallel computers are therefore more in the nature of an extension (of course, an important and significant extension) of the use of conventional computers.

In contrast, as we have seen, the architecture of neural networks represents a significant departure from the architecture of conventional computers. It is because of a possible confusion in this regard that an earlier name for neural networks, namely parallel distributed processing, has been largely displaced by the terms connectionist computing or neural computing/networks.

The design of a multilayered feedforward network and a basic understanding of how it functions are important parts of understanding neural computing. The central idea is that such networks operate with input patterns or vectors, matching them to output patterns or vectors. The process of matching each input pattern to an output pattern is a process of *classification*. One could also call it a process of *decoding* the input signals and *categorizing* them.

The important and valuable property of the networks is that this process is not based on using explicit rules to be provided by a programmer. The networks are based on a trial-and-error process of finding the weights that should be used in the context of the trial set of data provided. Inherent in this process is the ability to deal with incomplete or distorted information and to generalize by finding the nearest approximation to the given input pattern. The development of the field was really accelerated by the emergence of the backpropagation method, which enables a feedforward network to learn from examples and generalize—the most important characteristics of neural networks, as mentioned before. Another vital concept is that of Hopfield networks and their probabilistic extension, Boltzmann machines. These are important in handling the problem of local minima.

The distinction between supervised learning, in which the network has targets for the results to be produced, and unsupervised learning,

in which there are no such targets, is another central concept. We saw that unsupervised learning is exemplified by Kohonen maps and adaptive resonance networks, in contrast to supervised learning as exemplified by a multilayer network using backpropagation. As of today, the majority of applications involve supervised learning. But unsupervised learning, which we could fairly say is a more sophisticated form of learning, seems likely to be of increasing importance in the future.

⇨ What next?

We have titled this chapter Etc. to indicate that it aims to give some general comments and the flavor of some aspects of the field not covered in the previous chapter. But by no means does this chapter give all of the other aspects of the field that have not been covered in the other chapters. The following are some of the areas that readers, depending on individual taste and preferences, might want to look into further.

Let's start by considering the implications of the fact that neural networks are simulated or implemented as models on a conventional computer. Such a simulation of a neural computer is obviously essentially a program that runs on the standard computer. A computer operates differently when it runs different programs, and this is often described by saying that each software package converts the same physical computer into a different *virtual machine*. It can function as a word-processing machine, a spreadsheet machine, a database machine, and so on.

Any program that can be run as software can also be embodied in a chip. Many computers offer word-processing programs, spreadsheet programs, and so on in the form of ROM chips that can be plugged into the computer. In the same way, neural network simulations make conventional computers into a virtual machine that is a neural computer. So chips that do backpropagation or operate as a Hopfield net could be used to reinforce standard computers. For tasks with well-defined procedures, conventional computers can carry them out much more quickly and efficiently than neural networks because the

latter typically work by trial-and-error. There is no advantage in using trial-and-error when there is a clearly definable solution procedure.

On the other hand, when the solution procedure is not clearly specifiable, neural computers come into their own. The next natural step is to combine the advantages of both by using neural network simulation programs either as "modules" that can be called by other programs or as chip-based software that can be used by conventional programs. Progress in this direction is really leading to the stage of making conventional programs and neural networks truly complementary, where the strengths of both can be combined effectively.

The computer and the brain

As discussed at the beginning of this book, there have been two branches of development in the field of neural computing: the engineering and the cognitive science approach. In this book, we have focused on the engineering aspect of neural computing. We have discussed neural computers as devices that do certain tasks very well.

However, in this chapter, we would like to make a few comments about the alternative way of looking at neural networks, as "cognition machines" or devices that help in studying the nature of human learning, intelligence, etc. The motivation for designing neural computers came from the analogy with the architecture of the brain. The great pioneers McCulloch and Pitts were fundamentally engaged in the study of brain function, and they proposed their artificial neuron as a model for brain neurons.

It is inevitable that progress in the engineering aspect of making systems that work leads to better understanding of the brain and of human cognition, and understanding in the latter field provides guidance for better engineering design of neural networks. The two aspects of neural networks are very closely linked. For example, from an engineering approach, the method of adjusting weights in relation to the error is a technique that intuitively makes sense, and most importantly, it works.

From a cognitive science point of view, the rule is something more. It is often called the *Hebb learning rule*. As early as the 1940s, the famous Canadian psychologist Donald Hebb had proposed that the process of learning in the human brain might be based on the fact that the connections or synapses between neurons are strengthened or weakened depending on whether they operate together or not in various operations of the brain. He saw association between them as the key to the association of ideas that is involved in human learning. At that time, there was not enough physical evidence to substantiate or reject the hypothesis. But subsequent work has shown evidence that such change in the strength of connections between neurons in the brain does occur. In other words, there is indeed a biological analogy for the error correction rule, or as it is sometimes called, the *Widrow-Hoff rule*, or the *generalized delta rule*.

Again, the revival of neural networks is associated with the publication of the two volumes of *Parallel Distributed Processing* (1986). These books are a collection of the works of the group of researchers in San Diego, of whom one of the most prominent is the psychologist David Rumelhart.

There are many more such examples that suggest that the two different angles to neural computing, the engineering and the psychological, are mutually reinforcing and complementary. The human brain, despite increasing knowledge about it over the years, still has many mysteries associated with it, and the study of neural networks seems likely to help elucidate some of these mysteries.

⇨ Suggestions for further reading

In various chapters, we have provided some key references. The literature in this field has become so extensive that even if we provide a bibliography of a few hundred items, it would still be incomplete. Fortunately, in the last few years, a handful of superb collections of articles have been published. These collections give most of the path-breaking writings in the field, such as Hopfield's or Rumelhart's papers, as well as excellent review articles and articles indicating the state of the art in various subfields. Please see the bibliography for more information.

⇨ Conclusion

The growth of neural computing during the last few years has been so explosive that some people have expressed the fear that there might be a considerable amount of hype involved, and not much substance. Even if there has sometimes been some overenthusiastic description of the field, it is worth noting that there is something fundamentally significant about neural computing.

The special capabilities of generalizing and learning from examples distinguish neural computers from extant computers. Because neural computers fulfill this important complementary role, it seems fair to say that they are here to stay and will play an important role. They also have the second important role of helping to understand the human brain. To adapt a saying of Winston Churchill's, we could say that the progress in this direction has not reached the end nor the beginning of the end, nor even the end of the beginning. But most certainly there has been a very promising beginning that we hope will fulfill the expectations it has raised.

Part 2

Program listings

Program listings,
instructions,
and comments

CHAPTER 7

THE programs discussed here are simple programs that illustrate various concepts covered in the first part of the book. These programs are written in C and should compile with any ANSI C compiler. The executable files are also included on the disk, and they should run on any PC-compatible system.

The programs are written in C, but they could have been written in Pascal or BASIC or many other languages. The programs avoid any peculiarities in C and should be easy to convert into your language of choice. You will need to know some of the syntax of C to do this.

⇨ SIGMOID: The sigmoid function

This program simply lets you type in the value of the gain, and then it prints out the values of the sigmoid function. The value of x runs from –5 to 5, increasing x by 0.5 each time through the for loop. By using a large gain, you can see how the sigmoid function approximates the hard threshold function.

```
/* sigmoid.c */

#include <stdio.h>
#include <stdlib.h>
#include <math.h>

void spc(int);
float sigm(float);

main(){

    float x,y,k;

    clrscr();
    puts("The gain of the sigmoid function is k.");
    puts("Please type in the value of k (<= 100):");
    scanf("%f",&k);

    for(x=-5.0;x<=5.0;x+=0.5){
      y= sigm(x*k);
        /* print out the values */
        printf("IN=%6.2f OUT=%6.4f  |",x,y);
        /* print out spaces and + for graph */
        spc(40.0*y+0.5);
      puts("+");
    }
```

```
} /* end main */

void spc(int n)      /* prints n spaces */
{ int i;
    for( i=1;i<=n;putchar(32),i++);

}

float sigm(float x)
/* returns the value of the sigma function */
{ float y;
    y=1.0/(1.0 + exp(-x));
    return(y);

}     /* end of sigmoid.c */
```

The parameters of this loop can be changed to alter the range or the increment of x. For example, the statement:

$$for(x=-2;x<=2;x+=0.25)$$

would print 17 lines, with x running from −2 to 2. Don't make the increment too small, or the table will not fit on the screen.

MCPITTS: McCulloch Pitts neuron

This program lets you choose the weights and threshold of a single neuron with two inputs. It then draws a simple diagram of the network and creates a chart that gives the output for all four possible input combinations.

```
                              /* MCPITTS.C */

int x1,x2,out;
float w1,w2,T;

main()
{
   clrscr();

   /*  Get weights and threshold */

   printf("Please enter weight 1: ");
```

```
    scanf("%f",&w1);
    printf("Please enter weight 2: ");
    scanf("%f",&w2);
    printf("Please enter the threshold: ");
    scanf("%f",&T);

    /* print weights and threshold
       and a simple graph */

printf("\n\n->(1)\\ \n           \\ %4.3f\n            \\\n",w1 );
printf("          (out) %4.3f ->\n",T);
printf("          /\n          / %4.3f\n->(2)/\n\n",w2);

    /* print table of inputs and outputs */

    printf("               inputs\n");
    printf("        X1              X2          output\n");
    for(x1=0;x1<2;x1++)
       for(x2=0;x2<2;x2++)
          { out=(w1*x1+w2*x2>=T);
             printf("         %d              %d             %d\n",x1,x2,out);
          }

}   /* end MCPITTS.C */
```

⇨ LEARNIT: How a neuron learns

The program LEARNIT demonstrates how a single artificial neuron
with two inputs can learn. It asks for four outputs for the four
possible input combinations. It lets you type in the initial weights, or
it randomly creates them. It also asks for the *correction factor*, the
amount the weights change. After you have given the program these
values, it cycles through the input combinations, correcting the
weights if the output is incorrect. You might find that this takes a long
time, especially if you choose a small correction factor. Just press the
Esc key to stop. Once it gets correct responses for all four input
combinations, it stops and prints the final weights.

```
/* learnit.c */
/* Perceptron Learning Program */

#include <stdio.h>
#include <stdlib.h>

int x[4][3]={{1,0,0},
       {1,1,0},
```

```
        {1,0,1},
        {1,1,1}};
/* The four possible inputs. X(0) is always 1 */

float w[3],corr;

int r[4],resp,diff,i,wrongresp=1,c;
char (choice);

main() {
    clrscr();
    for (i=0;i<4;i++)
    { printf("Type in the correct response for these inputs %d %d:"
            ,x[i][1],x[i][2]);
     scanf("%d",&r[i]);
    } /* get the desired responses for the possible inputs %d %d:"

puts("Type 1 to assign your own weights or 2 to have the weights");
puts("assigned randomly.");

if (choice=getch()=='1') {

    printf("first weight\n");
    scanf("%f",&w[1]);
    printf("second weight\n");
    scanf("%f",&w[2]);
    printf("zeroth weight (-1 times the threshold)\n");
    scanf("%f",&w[0]); }

else {     /* assign the weights randomly */

    randomize();
    w[0]=random(1000)/1000.0;
    w[1]=random(1000)/1000.0;
    w[2]=random(1000)/1000.0;}

 printf("\nThe initial weights are %f %f %f\n",w[1],w[2],w[0]);

 printf("\nWhat is the value of your correction factor? ");
 scanf("%f",&corr);
 printf("\n");

 while (wrongresp){ /* loop until all responses are correct */
    wrongresp=0;    /* set flag for no wrong responses */
    for (i=0;i<4;i++){
         resp=((w[0]*x[i][0]+w[1]*x[i][1]+w[2]*x[i][2])>=0);
         diff=r[i]-resp;

        printf("test inputs %d %d, response %d, correct response  %d.\n"
                ,x[i][0],x[i][1],resp,r[i]);

        if (diff!=0) { /* If the response is wrong,
                         adjust weights and set the flag.*/
```

```
        wrongresp=1;
        w[0]=w[0]+diff*corr*x[i][0];
          w[1]=w[1]+diff*corr*x[i][1];
          w[2]=w[2]+diff*corr*x[i][2];
          printf("New weights %f %f %f \n\n",w[1],w[2],w[0]);
          }
      else
          printf("No adjustment necessary\n\n");       /* end if */
      puts("Press ESC to end, any other key to continue\n");
        c=getch();
        if(c==27) return(0); /* exit if the user presses ESC */

      }   /* end for */

  } /* end while */

    /* All responses are correct. Print out the weights. */

  printf("The final weights are w1=%f w2=%f w0=%f \n\n",w[1],w[2],w[0]);

  }     /* end LEARNIT.C */
```

SIGRESP: Responsiveness of the sigmoid function

The program SIGRESP lets you see the change in the sigmoid function from a change in x of size h. If h is small and y=f(x), then the change in f should be approximately h * y * (1 – y). Because of the way computers must round off floating point numbers, if you make h too small in this program, you will get strange results. Try various values for h and see what happens.

```
/* sigresp.c */

#include <stdio.h>
#include <stdlib.h>
#include <math.h>

float sigm(float);

main(){

    float x,y,h,diff;

    clrscr();
    printf("What do you wish to use for h?");
    scanf("%f",&h);
```

```
     printf("The value of h, the change in the input, is %6.4f.\n",h);

     for(x=-5.0;x<=5.0;x+=0.5){
         y=sigm(x);
         diff=sigm(x+h)-y;

       printf("IN=%6.2f OUT=%6.4f          increase/h=%6.4f  OUT*(1-OUT)=%6.4f\n"
               ,x,y,diff/h,y*(1.0-y));
     }

} /* end main */

float sigm(float x)
{ float y;
     y=1.0/(1.0 + exp(-x));
     return(y);

} /* end sigresp.c */
```

SUMSQ: How error changes as weights are changed

SUMSQ is a simple little program that demonstrates how changes in x changes $(r - x)^2$. It is easy to see that the closer x is to r, the smaller the change. The program asks you for the correct response, r, and the minimum and maximum values of x. It makes the increment h equal to one-sixteenth of the range of x. It then prints a chart of x, the squared error, and the amount of change from the last squared error.

```
/* SUMSQ.C
   Experiment with changes in the sum of squares */

#include <stdio.h>

main()    {
        float xmin,xmax,x,r,h,diff,newss,oldss;
        clrscr();
        printf("What is the correct response (r)? ");
        scanf("%f",&r);
        printf("What is the minimum value of x? ");
        scanf("%f",&xmin);
        printf("What is the maximum value of x? ");
        scanf("%f",&xmax);
        h=(xmax-xmin)/16.0;
        x=xmin;
        oldss=(r-x)*(r-x);
```

```
      printf("   x         squared error    change   \n");
      printf("%8.4f     %8.4f \n",x,oldss);
      for(x=x+h;x<=xmax;x+=h) {
          newss=(r-x)*(r-x);
          diff=newss-oldss;
          printf("%8.4f      %8.4f      %8.4f     \n",x,newss,diff);
          oldss=newss;
      }

} /* end sumsq.c */
```

⇨ BACKPROP: How backpropogation works

BACKPROP is one of the longer programs we will look at. It tries to find a set of weights to solve the XOR problem using two input nodes, two hidden nodes, and one output node. It asks you for the correction factor and how many iterations to correct the weights before it gives up. It normally stops when the MSE (mean squared error) falls below 0.01. To simplify things and put more importance on recent squared errors, MSE is computed by taking the old MSE times 0.9 plus the new error squared times 0.1. In other words:

$$\text{New MSE} = 0.9 * \text{Old MSE} + 0.1 * \text{New Error}^2$$

$$= \text{Old MSE} + 0.1 * (\text{New Error}^2 - \text{Old MSE})$$

This method of updating MSE is identical to a forecasting method known as *exponential smoothing*.

The program halts with a good solution most of the time. Because it randomly sets the initial weights and randomly picks the input pattern to use next, it sometimes halts without a good solution. If it got stuck in a local minimum, the program would go through all the iterations without the MSE getting small. This usually results in two inputs that result in the correct output and two inputs that give outputs that are near 0.5. It also might have gotten a low MSE only because the last inputs that were randomly picked gave low errors, and the ones with high errors didn't get picked.

You might ask why the program doesn't deterministically cycle through all the input pairs in order. The problem is that the weights might periodically go through four sets of values and never converge to a good solution.

```c
/* backprop.c */
/* Back Propogation */
#include <stdio.h>
#include <stdlib.h>
#include <math.h>

float w03,w04,w05,
      w13,w14,w23,w24,w35,w45,
      act3,act4,act5,
      out3,out4,out5,
      cr3,cr4,cr5,
      beta,r5,error,mse=1;

/* The variables :
   w - the weights
   act - the activization levels of the nodes
   out - the outputs of the nodes
   cr - the corrections, multiplied by beta
   mse - mean squared error
   r5 - the correct response (output) from node 5
*/

float sig(float);

main(){

int i,in1,in2,iters;

puts("What is the correction factor?");
scanf("%f",&beta);

/* What is the maximum number of iterations? */
puts("How many iterations?");
scanf("%d",&iters);

randomize();

/* randomly set the weights */

w03=random(1000)/100.0-5.0;
w04=random(1000)/100.0-5.0;
w05=random(1000)/100.0-5.0;
w13=random(1000)/100.0-5.0;
w14=random(1000)/100.0-5.0;
w23=random(1000)/100.0-5.0;
```

```
w24=random(1000)/100.0-5.0;
w35=random(1000)/100.0-5.0;
w45=random(1000)/100.0-5.0;

for(i=1;(i<=iters)&&(mse>.01);i++) {

    /* stop when the number of iterations is too large
       or when the MSE is small */

    in1=random(2);
    in2=random(2);
    act3=w13*in1+w23*in2+w03;
    out3=sig(act3);
    act4=w14*in1+w24*in2+w04;
    out4=sig(act4);
    act5=w35*out3+w45*out4+w05;
    out5=sig(act5);
    r5=in1+in2-2.00*in1*in2;
    error=r5-out5;
    mse=mse+.1*(error*error-mse);

    cr5 = error*out5*(1.0-out5);
    w05 = w05+beta*cr5;
    w35 = w35 + (beta*cr5*out3);
    w45 = w45 + (beta*cr5*out4);

    cr3 = w35*cr5*out3*(1.0-out3);
    cr4 = w45*cr5*out4*(1.0-out4);

    w03 = w03 + (beta*cr3);
    w04 = w04 + (beta*cr4);

    w13 = w13 + (beta*cr3*in1);
    w14 = w14 + (beta*cr4*in1);
    w23 = w23 + (beta*cr3*in2);
    w24 = w24 + (beta*cr4*in2);


    printf( "i=%d input= %d %d output=%10.5f  mse=%10.5f\n"
            ,i,in1,in2,out5,mse);

}   /* end for loop */

/* print out the weights */

printf("\nw03=%10.5f    w13=%10.5f    w23=%10.5f\n",w03,w13,w23);
printf("w04=%10.5f    w14=%10.5f    w24=%10.5f\n",w04,w14,w24);
printf("w05=%10.5f    w35=%10.5f    w45=%10.5f\n",w05,w35,w45);

} /* end main */

float sig(float x)
```

```
{   float y;
    y=1.0/(1.0+exp(-x));
    return(y);
}   /* end function sig */

/* end backprop.c */
```

⇨ HOPONE: Hopfield network

The program HOPONE asks you for three patterns (*A*, *B*, and *C*) of eight bits (0s or 1s) and a test pattern *X*. It then computes a set of weights for the eight nodes. Finally, it randomly selects bits (or nodes) of *X* and changes the bit according to the weights. It repeats this until no more changes are necessary or possible. The pattern has then converged to a stable pattern.

The ending pattern will many times be one of the patterns *A*, *B*, or *C*. Sometimes it will not. Because we are using only eight nodes, we can only reliably store 8 *.15 = 1.2 patterns. Three patterns are a bit much to ask for. Sometimes even one of the patterns *A*, *B*, or *C* used as *X* will converge to something else.

```
/* HOPONE.C */
#include <stdio.h>
#include <stdlib.h>

#define NUMPTS 8

main(){
   int ax[NUMPTS+1],bx[NUMPTS+1],cx[NUMPTS+1],
       ay[NUMPTS+1],by[NUMPTS+1],cy[NUMPTS+1],
       x[NUMPTS+1],y[NUMPTS+1],t[NUMPTS+1][NUMPTS+1];

/* The variables x, ax, bx, and cx store the patterns
   as 0's or 1's. The variables y, ay, by, and cy
   store the same patterns as -1's and 1's. */

   int i,j,k,act,converge;

   printf("Type in the patterns like this:\n0 1 1 1 0 0 1 0\n\n");

   printf("Type in the first (A) pattern:  \n");
   for (i=1;i<=NUMPTS;scanf("%d",&ax[i++]));
```

```
printf("--------------\n");
for (i=1;i<=NUMPTS;printf("%d ",ax[i++]));

printf("\n\nType in the second (B) pattern:  \n");
for (i=1;i<=NUMPTS;scanf("%d",&bx[i++]));
printf("--------------\n");
for (i=1;i<=NUMPTS;printf("%d ",bx[i++]));

printf("\n\nType in the third (C) pattern:  \n");
for (i=1;i<=NUMPTS;scanf("%d",&cx[i++]));
printf("--------------\n");
for (i=1;i<=NUMPTS;printf("%d ",cx[i++]));

printf ("\n\nType in the test (X) pattern:  \n");
for (i=1;i<=NUMPTS;scanf("%d",&x[i++]));
printf("--------------\n");
for (i=1;i<=NUMPTS;printf("%d ",x[i++]));

printf("\n");

for(i=1;i<=NUMPTS;i++) {
     ay[i]=2*ax[i]-1;
     by[i]=2*bx[i]-1;
     cy[i]=2*cx[i]-1;
      y[i]=2*x[i] -1;
}


/* compute the weights */

for (i=1;i<=NUMPTS;i++)
   for(j=i;j<=NUMPTS;j++){
      if (j==i) t[i][j]=0;
      else {
         t[i][j]=ay[i]*ay[j]+by[i]*by[j]+cy[i]*cy[j];
         t[j][i]=t[i][j];
      }
}

  puts("\nNow revising pattern...\n");


/* randomly revise nodes */

randomize();

converge=0;

while(!converge) {
     /* Loop until the pattern stabilizes. */


  i=random(NUMPTS)+1; /* Pick a node at random */
```

```
    /* update node i */
    act=0;
    for (j=1;j<=NUMPTS;j++) act+=t[i][j]*y[j];
    y[i]=2*(act>=0)-1;
    /* +1 if act >=0m -1 otherwise */

    for (j=1;j<=NUMPTS;printf("%d ",(y[j++]> 0)));
    printf(" .... i= %d  \n",i);
    /* check for convergence */
    converge=1;  /* set flag */
    for(k=1;k<=NUMPTS;k++){
       act=0;
       for (j=1;j<=NUMPTS;j++) act+=t[j][k]*y[j];
       converge*=(y[k]==(2*(act>=0)-1)); /* revise flag */
    }

  } /* end while loop */


  printf("The final pattern is\n");
  for (i=1;i<=NUMPTS;printf("%d ",(y[i++]>0)));

} /* end HOPONE.C */
```

⇨ HOPTWO: Assignment problem using a Hopfield net

The program HOPTWO finds the solution to the 4 × 4 assignment problem described in part I of the text. It asks you for 16 values, the costs of the combinations of four workers and four tasks. The numbers are entered as rows of four numbers each. It then randomly assigns a zero or one to each node. It then randomly chooses nodes and computes their activization values and updates them. BigM is the largest of the costs, and it is used in the weights. The weights between nodes in the same rows and columns are inhibitory and equal −2 * BigM. The bias weights are positive and equal BigM minus the cost of the node. These bias weights are the weights from node 0, which is always on, and they are −1 times the threshold of each node. The network quickly finds a feasible solution, i.e., one that has one assignment in each row and column, but not necessarily the optimal one. The problem is that the network might get stuck in a local minimum.

```
/* HOPTWO.C */
#include <stdio.h>
#include <stdlib.h>

main(){
   float m[5][5],act,bigm=-100,sum=0.0;
   int x[5][5],i1,i2,j1,j2,i,j,k;

   randomize();


   puts("Type in the rows of costs like this:");
   puts("12 13.6 16 23.1");

   /* get costs and initialize nodes */

   for (i=1;i<5;i++){
     printf("What are the costs for row %d?\n",i);
     for(j=1;j<5;j++) {
        scanf("%f",&m[i][j]);
        if (m[i][j]>bigm) bigm=m[i][j];   /* find biggest cost */
        x[i][j]=random(2);       /* initialize node randomly */
     }
   }

/* randomly update nodes */

   for (k=1;k<=250;k++){
     i1=random(4)+1;
     j1=random(4)+1;
     printf("old x%d%d = %d   ",i1,j1,x[i1][j1]);

     act=2*bigm-m[i1][j1]; /* threshold bias */

     for (i2=1;i2<5;i2++) if (i2!=i1) act-=2*bigm*x[i2][j1];
     /* inhibition from the row */

     for (j2=1;j2<5;j2++) if (j2!=j1) act-=2*bigm*x[i1][j2];
     /* inhibition from the column */

     x[i1][j1]=(act>=0.0);
     printf("Activization = %10.5f  new x%d%d = %d \n",act,i1,j1,x[i1][j1]);

   } /* end k loop */

   printf ("\nThe final assignments are: \n\n");
   for (i=1;i<5;i++){

     for(j=1;j<5;j++) {
        printf(" %d ",x[i][j] );
        sum+=x[i][j]*m[i][j];
     }
     printf("\n");
```

```
    }

    printf("\nThe total cost is %7.4f \n",sum);


} /* end main */

float sig(float x)
{    float y;
     y=1.0/(1.0+exp(-x));
     return(y);
}    /* end function sig */
```

 BOLTZ: Boltzmann machine

The program BOLTZ tries to deal with the shortcoming of HOPTWO—getting stuck in a local minimum. It uses the concepts of Boltzmann machines and simulated annealing to escape from local minima. After getting the costs, the program randomly assigns the nodes' values of zero or one as before. It also sets the temperature t to a high value. Each time through the loop, the program randomly picks a node and computes its activization value. It then sets p to the value of the sigmoid function with its argument equal to the activization divided by t. The variable p has some value between zero and one. It is greater than 0.5 if the activization is positive, and less than 0.5 if it is negative. The variable u is a uniformly distributed random variable. The node is changed to one if $u<=p$. This means that the node becomes one with probability p and zero with probability $u>p$. Nodes with positive activizations are more likely to become one rather than zero, and conversely for nodes with negative activizations.

While the program goes through the loop, the temperature is also slowly being lowered 3% each time through the loop. The lower the temperature, the more the sigmoid function approximates the hard threshold function. The lower the temperature, the less likely the network will move to a higher energy state because p will be close to zero or close to one.

You might want to experiment with different ways of decreasing the temperature. If the temperature gets too small, however, you might

find that the exponential function used in the function sig will
generate an overflow error.

```c
/* BOLTZ.C */

#include <stdio.h>
#include <stdlib.h>
#include <math.h>

float sig(float);

main(){
  float m[5][5],act,bigm=-100,u,p,t,sum;
  int x[5][5],i1,i2,j1,j2,i,j,k;

  randomize();


  puts("Type in the rows of costs like this:");
  puts("12 13.6 16 23.1");

  /* get costs and initialize nodes */

  for (i=1;i<5;i++){
    printf("What are the costs for row %d?\n",i);
    for(j=1;j<5;j++) {
       scanf("%f",&m[i][j]);
       if (m[i][j]>bigm) bigm=m[i][j];    /* find biggest cost */
       x[i][j]=random(2);        /* initialize node */
    }
  }

  t=bigm*10.0;  /* initialize temperature */


/* randomly update nodes */

  for (k=1;k<=250;k++){
    i1=random(4)+1;
    j1=random(4)+1;
    printf("old x%d%d = %d  ",i1,j1,x[i1][j1]);

    act=2*bigm-m[i1][j1];
    for (i2=1;i2<5;i2++) if (i2!=i1) act-=2*bigm*x[i2][j1];
    for (j2=1;j2<5;j2++) if (j2!=j1) act-=2*bigm*x[i1][j2];
    p=sig(act/t);
    u=random(1000)/1000.0;
    x[i1][j1]=(u<=p);

    printf("Activization = %10.5f  new x%d%d = %d \n",act,i1,j1,x[i1][j1]);
```

```
    t=t*0.97; /* revise temperature */
    /* The above line decreases t geometrically.
       Modify this if you wish, but don't let
       t become negative or zero!    */
  } /* end k loop */

  printf ("\nThe final assignments are: \n\n");
  for (i=1;i<5;i++){

    for(j=1;j<5;j++) {
        printf(" %d ",x[i][j]);
        sum+=x[i][j]*m[i][j];
    }
    printf("\n");

  }
  printf ("\nThe total cost is %7.4f\n",sum);


} /* end main */

float sig(float x)
{   float y;
    y=1.0/(1.0+exp(-x));
    return(y);
}    /* end function sig */
```

KOHONEN: Feature map using a Kohonen network

The program KOHONEN adjusts the weights of 100 nodes in a 10×10 array to identify three patterns. The program actually has a grid of 12×12 nodes. The middle 10×10 grid of nodes are the ones used. The reason for this larger grid is to avoid having to deal with nodes on the edges or corners. Because all of the nodes on the 10×10 grid are in the interior, we don't need to worry about this. Also, the nodes have only one index as defined, but we can access them with double indices by using the function INDEX. This is also done for convenience to avoid triple indices for the weights.

The three patterns or vectors that are learned have coordinates within 1×1 squares centered around the points (0,3), (3,3), and (3,0). Each time through the loop, one of these three points is picked, and then a random offset, uniformly distributed between −0.5 and 0.5, is added to

each coordinate. The program then normalizes the vector and finds the closest node. This requires many floating point operations, and it is what makes the program run slowly if you do not have a math coprocessor. It then adjusts the weights of the best-fitting node and the eight nodes surrounding it, above, below, left, right, or diagonally. Finally it prints three diagrams or feature maps, showing with an asterisk which nodes are closest to each of the three prototype test vectors. Because all three feature maps cannot fit on the screen at once, you might want to use the Print Screen key to print out a screen dump of the first two maps and then again when the third map is displayed.

```c
#include <stdio.h>
#include <math.h>
#include <stdlib.h>

float w[3][144],w1,w2,testx,testy,dist,bestdist;
int i,j,k,c,besti=0,bestj=0;

int index(int i,int j);
void normalize(float *x, float *y);

main(){
    /* initialize weights */
    clrscr();
    puts("Please wait.  This takes a while.");
    randomize();
    for (j=0;j<144;j++) {
        w1=random(1000)/1000.0-0.5;
        w2=random(1000)/1000.0-0.5;
        normalize(&w1,&w2);
        w[1][j]=w1;
        w[2][j]=w2;
    }

    /* adjust weights */
        for (k=1;k<=100;k++){
          testx=0;testy=0;
          while (testx+testy == 0) {
            testx=3*random(2)+random(1000)/1000.00-0.5;
            testy=3*random(2)+random(1000)/1000.00-0.5;
          }
        normalize(&testx,&testy);

        /* find the closest node */

        bestdist=10.0;
        for(i=1;i<=10;i++)
          for(j=1;j<=10;j++){
```

```
                dist=2-2*(testx*w[1][index(i,j)]+testy*w[2][index(i,j)]);

                if (dist<bestdist) {
                    besti=i;
                    bestj=j;
                    bestdist=dist;
                }    /* end if */
        }     /* end for loops */

    /* adjust weights */

    for (i=besti-1;i<=besti+1;i++)
        for (j=bestj-1;j<=bestj+1;j++) {
            w[1][index(i,j)]=(w[1][index(i,j)]+testx)/2.0;
            w[2][index(i,j)]=(w[2][index(i,j)]+testy)/2.0;
            normalize(&w[1][index(i,j)],&w[2][index(i,j)]);
        }   /* end for loops */

    }            /* go get another test point */

    clrscr();

    for(k=1;k<=3;k++){
     printf("Press a key for pattern %d.\n",k);
     getch();
     testx=k % 2 ;
     testy=(k/2) ;
     normalize(&testx,&testy);

     for (i=1; i<=10 ;i++)
        for(j=1;j<=10;j++){
            dist=2-2*(testx*w[1][index(i,j)]+testy*w[2][index(i,j)]);
            if (dist<.1) c='*';
            else c='-';


            printf("%c",c);
        }   /* end j loop */
        printf("\n");

    }     /* end i loop */
    } /* end k loop */

11.

} /* end main */

int index(int i, int j) {
    int k;
    k=12*i+j;
    return(k);
}    /* end of index function */
```

```
void normalize(float *x, float *y){
    float dist;
    dist=sqrt(*x**x + *y**y);
    *x=*x/dist;
    *y=*y/dist;
} /*end normalize */
```

⇨ MATRIX: A matrix multiplication program

The program MATRIX multiplies two matrices together and displays the result. It first asks the user for the sizes of the two matrices, reminding the user that the number of columns of the first matrix must equal the number of rows of the second. It then asks the user to type in the elements of the matrices a row at a time. Finally, it computes the product and displays the results.

The first matrix is stored in the array a. The second is put in the array b, and the product is stored in array c. The arrays are 10×10, so up to 10×10 matrices can be handled. Internally, the indices start at 0, but to the user they start at the more traditional 1. The final result stored in the array c is really unnecessary for this program because its elements are printed on the fly and stored in the variable x. If you wish to extend this program, however, the array c contains the product and can be used for further calculations.

The program can be easily modifiable to calculate the sum of two matrices, the transpose of a matrix, or the product of a scalar and a matrix. All of these tasks are simpler to accomplish than the product of two matrices. Finding the inverse of a square matrix is another matter. You should consult a good linear algebra book to find out how to invert a matrix.

```
#include <stdio.h>
#include <stdlib.h>

main(){
  float a[10][10],b[10][10],c[10][10],x;
  int i,j,k,rows1,cols1,rows2,cols2;
```

```
      puts("The matrices can be up to 10x10 in size.");
      puts("How many rows does the first matrix have?");
      scanf("%d",&rows1);
      puts("The number of columns of the first matrix must");
      puts("equal the number of rows in the second matrix.");
      puts("What is this number?");
      scanf("%d",&cols1);
      rows2=cols1;
      puts("How many columns does the second matrix have?");
      scanf("%d",&cols2);

      puts("Type in the rows of the matrices like this:");
      puts("12 13.6 16 23.1");

      puts("\nInput the first matrix.");

      for(i=0;i<rows1;i++){
        printf("What are the values for row %d?\n",i+1);
        for(j=0;j<cols1;j++)    scanf("%f",&a[i][j]);
      }

      puts("\nInput the second matrix.");

      for (i=0;i<rows2;i++){
        printf("What are the values for row %d?\n",i+1);
        for(j=0;j<cols2;j++)    scanf("%f",&b[i][j]);
      }

  /*      Now let's multiply the matrices.          */
      puts("\nThe result is \n");
      for (i=0;i<rows1;i++){
        for(j=0;j<cols2;j++){
            x=0.0;
            for(k=0;k<cols1;k++) x+=a[i][k]*b[k][j];
            c[i][j]=x;
            printf(" %7.3f",x);

        }
        puts("");
  }

  } /* end main */
```

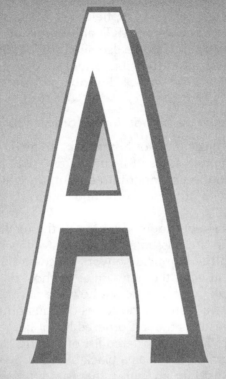

Neural networks
and matrices

APPENDIX A

W E have seen that there are different types of neural networks: feedforward networks, Hopfield networks, Boltzmann machines, Kohonen networks, ART, and others we have not discussed in this book. We have also seen the details of how these work in different ways. At the same time, they do have some essential similarities. One way of describing these similarities would be as follows:

> ➤ All of the networks operate on an ordered list of input values.

> ➤ Each of the basic units of a network, an artificial neuron or AN, forms a weighted sums of its inputs and uses a transfer function to transform the net input into an output, which in turn would be the input to other neurons, and so on.

Let's ignore the stage-by-stage operation of the feedforward network, in which the signals are passed on to successive layers, and let's ignore the steps by which the Hopfield network successively changes state. Instead, let's look at what the network as a whole does. From the outside, so to speak, we can describe how the network functions in the following terms. As a result of the series of transformations in the network, the net result is that an ordered list of inputs is fed to a network, and it produces an ordered list of outputs. In other words, we can think of a neural network as a black box that transforms an input that is an ordered list into an output that is a different ordered list.

At various places in this book, we have seen that such transformations of a list of inputs into a list of outputs is closely connected with important practical problems: it is the fundamental operation of recognizing objects based on an input list of features and categorizing them by assigning them an appropriate output list. We could call this output list a *category indicator* or label. As we saw, this is a central problem to be addressed in picture or voice recognition and so forth. In fact, we could say that categorization or classification is a key part of most decision making.

We can think of decision making in the broadest sense as classifying a problem appropriately using its "input list" of relevant features and thereby identifying the appropriate "output list," i.e., details of the solution to be adopted for that problem. A well-established field of study that deals with such transformations of lists of values into other

lists of values is the field of knowledge called *matrix algebra*. (For anyone proceeding to further study of neural networks, a knowledge of matrix algebra is almost indispensable. This appendix is provided as a starting point for such knowledge.)

⇨ Basic definitions: matrix and matrix operations

For our purposes, we can define an "*m* by *n* matrix of real numbers" as follows: It is a rectangular table or ARRAY, with *m* rows and *n* columns, and each of the *n* items in each of the *m* rows is a real number. A real number is just the numbers we usually encounter in connection with physical measurements, both positive and negative. Examples would be whole numbers like 7 or –9, or fractions or decimals like –⅗ or 4.26, or mathematical constants like pi or *e*.

Real numbers are distinguished from complex numbers. At this stage, we will note only that they involve, in addition to the real numbers, the mathematical constant *i*, which is defined as having the property that *i* squared = –1. In the rest of the chapter, when we talk of a matrix, it is implied that it is a matrix of real numbers, unless it is specifically mentioned otherwise.

The items in the matrix are also called the *elements* of the matrix. (The fact that we have specifically referred to a matrix of real numbers naturally implies that the elements of a matrix could be complex numbers or other types of entities as well, in the relaxant contexts and applications.) An *m* by *n* matrix is also described as a matrix of dimensions *m* by *n*. An example of a 3-by-2 matrix would be the array with 3 rows and 2 columns:

$$\begin{bmatrix} 2 & 0.5 \\ -1 & 1.2 \\ 4 & 7 \end{bmatrix}$$

We use the rectangular brackets to indicate that what is enclosed between them is a matrix.

We can look more closely at the pattern of a matrix and think of each row as being itself a matrix: each row in the previous example is clearly a table or array of numbers with 1 row and 2 columns, so it is a "1-by-2 matrix," according to the basic definition of a matrix as given above. An alternative name for a matrix with just one row is to call it a *row vector*, and we will use the terms row vector and row of the matrix interchangeably. For example,

$$[\quad 2 \quad 7 \quad -1 \quad 5 \quad]$$

is a row vector with four elements or numbers in it. We can call it a matrix of dimensions 1 by 4. Alternatively, it is said to be a row vector of dimension 4.

The items or elements in a row vector are also sometimes called the *components* of the vector. Similarly, each column of an m by n matrix can be thought of as a matrix of dimensions m by 1. If some matrix has a column:

$$\begin{bmatrix} 1 \\ -5 \\ 4 \end{bmatrix}$$

we can call it a 3-by-1 matrix, or a *column vector* of dimension 3. The column vector obtained by writing the elements of the row as a column is called the *transpose* of the row. The transpose of:

$$[\quad 2 \quad 7 \quad -1 \quad 5 \quad]$$

is

$$\begin{bmatrix} 2 \\ 7 \\ -1 \\ 5 \end{bmatrix}$$

And in exactly the same way, the transpose of a column vector is a row vector.

The idea of transposing can be extended to a matrix that has more than one row and more than one column. In that case, if each row of the original matrix is transposed to give a column, the matrix with these columns is called the transpose of the original matrix. It is clear that if we transpose a matrix with m rows and n columns, the transpose will have n elements in each column, and m such columns, so it will have dimensions n by m. For example, the transpose of the 3-by-2 matrix given earlier would be a 2-by-3 matrix as:

$$\begin{bmatrix} 2 & -1 & 4 \\ 0.5 & 1.2 & 7 \end{bmatrix}$$

Certain definitions used for matrices are intuitively reasonable. Two matrices are said to be equal if and only if they have the same dimensions and each element in one is equal to the element in the same row and column position in the other. Just as with ordinary numbers, arithmetic operations are defined for the collection of numbers as a whole, which we call a matrix. The sum of two matrices is obtained by summing the elements in the corresponding positions: e.g., the sum of the matrices:

$$\begin{bmatrix} a & b \\ c & d \end{bmatrix}$$

and

$$\begin{bmatrix} p & q \\ r & s \end{bmatrix}$$

is the matrix:

$$\begin{bmatrix} a+p & b+q \\ c+r & d+s \end{bmatrix}$$

It is clear we can add two matrices if and only if they have the same number of rows and columns, to enable us to add the elements in the corresponding row and column positions. In the same way, we can subtract one matrix from another if they have the same dimensions: the resulting matrix has elements that are generated by subtracting elements in corresponding positions.

⇨ Multiplication of matrices

The most important operation defined with matrices is multiplication. On the basis of how matrices are added and subtracted, you might expect that the product of two matrices would be defined only if both matrices have the same dimensions, and that the elements of the product matrix would be obtained by multiplying corresponding elements. However, a different definition of multiplication has been found to be much more useful and let's consider this now.

We start with a basic definition: The product of a row vector on the left and a column vector on the right is defined only if they have the dimension or same number of elements in each of them. In that case, the product of the row vector:

$$[\ r1\ \ r2\ \ r3\ ]$$

and the column vector:

$$\begin{bmatrix} c1 \\ c2 \\ c3 \end{bmatrix}$$

is defined as the sum r1 * c1 + r2 * c2 + r3 * c3, i.e., we multiply the first element in the row by the first element in the column, the second element in the row by the second element in the column . . . and so on, and add up all the products. We see that this will work only if the row and the column have the same number of elements, i.e., the same dimension. Also, the result is just a single number. (We could also call the column vector as transp ([c1 c2 c3]) where transp is short for transpose.) For example, the product of the row:

$$[\quad 2 \quad 3 \quad 4 \quad]$$

on the left and the column:

$$\begin{bmatrix} -1 \\ 2 \\ 5 \end{bmatrix}$$

on the right would be:

$$2 * -1 + 3 * 2 + 4 * 5 = 24$$

With this notation we see that the weighted sums of inputs that are formed by each neuron in a neural network, such as:

$$w1 * X1 + w2 * X2 + w3 * X3$$

can be thought of as the product of the row vector:

$$[\quad X1 \quad X2 \quad X3 \quad]$$

and the column vector:

$$\begin{bmatrix} w1 \\ w2 \\ w3 \end{bmatrix} \quad \text{or transp([w1 w2 w3])}$$

Of course, we can also think of the product as the product of the row vector:

$$[\ w1 \quad w2 \quad w3\ ]$$

and the column vector:

$$\begin{bmatrix} X1 \\ X2 \\ X3 \end{bmatrix}$$

We get the same result either way.

It is often convenient to denote a whole row vector by a single symbol, say $X^\sim$, to denote the whole row:

$$[\ X1\ X2\ X3\ ]$$

with the understanding that this is a vector and not a single number. Similarly, $w^\sim$ could be used to denote the vector:

$$[\ w1 \quad w2 \quad w3 \ldots\ ]$$

You could use a symbol like $R^\sim$ to indicate a whole matrix.

Another operation defined for a row or column vector is called *scalar multiplication*. This is the multiplication of a vector by a single number or scalar. For example, the product of the number 5 and the row vector:

$$[\ 3 \ -2 \ 5 \ ]$$

is:

$$[\ 15 \ -10 \ 25 \ ]$$

We multiply each component of the vector by the number 5. To put it another way, in scalar multiplication we "scale up" each component of the vector, in this case by a factor of 5. A matrix with more than one row and more than one column can also be scalar multiplied: the scalar product of 3 and the matrix:

$$\begin{bmatrix} 1 & 8 \\ 2 & 5 \end{bmatrix}$$

is:

$$\begin{bmatrix} 3 & 24 \\ 6 & 15 \end{bmatrix}$$

When multiplying a matrix or row or column by a scalar, we can write the scalar on either side of the matrix:

$$3 * \begin{bmatrix} 1 & 8 \\ 2 & 5 \end{bmatrix}$$

would be the same as:

$$\begin{bmatrix} 1 & 8 \\ 2 & 5 \end{bmatrix} * 3$$

Unlike when multiplying matrices, we do not have to be concerned about which is on the right and which is on the left.

The definition given previously for the product of a row vector and a column vector is first extended to define the product of a row vector

on the left and a matrix with more than 1 row and column on the right. Suppose the row vector on the left is:

$$[\quad 3 \quad 2 \quad 5 \quad]$$

and the matrix R~ on the right is:

$$\begin{bmatrix} 1 & 3 \\ 2 & -1 \\ 4 & 2 \end{bmatrix}$$

The product is defined as follows: Multiply the row vector on the left and the first column of R~:

$$3 * 1 + 2 * 2 + 5 * 4 = 27$$

Next multiply the row vector on the left and the second column of R~:

$$3 * 3 + 2 * -1 + 5 * 2 = 17$$

(If there are more columns in R~, keep repeating for column 3, column 4 . . .)

Write down all the results as a row. In this case we have the row:

$$[\quad 27 \quad 17 \quad]$$

Note that this will work only if there are as many columns in the row vector on the left as there are elements in each of the columns on the right. To put it another way, the row vector on the left must have the same dimension as each of the columns in R~, for as we saw earlier, this is necessary for the basic operation of multiplying a row and a column. This is sometimes described by saying that the row and the column are *conformable for multiplication* only if they have the same dimension. We can see that the result will be a row with as many elements as there are columns in R~, since each column in R~ generates one number in the result row.

Once we have defined how to multiply a row vector on the left with a matrix like R~ on the right, we can extend the operations to multiplying two matrices when the left matrix has more than one row. We saw that we multiply a row on the left and R~ by multiplying each column of R~ in turn. If instead of just a single row, we have a matrix on the left, which we might call L~, we generate a row for the result by first multiplying the first row of L~ and the matrix R~ as before. We then use the second row of L~, multiply R~ to get a second row for the result or product matrix, and so on, until all the rows of L~ have been used. We will end up with as many rows as there are rows in the left matrix, since each row of the left matrix generates one row in the result matrix. And, as mentioned before, we will end up with as many columns as there are columns in the right matrix, since one column is generated for each column in the right matrix.

So, for example, if we multiply a 4-by-7 matrix L~ on the left by a 7-by-3 matrix R~ on the right, we will end up with 4 rows and 3 columns, i.e., the result is a 4-by-3 matrix. Note that the 7 matching of the 7s in 4-by-7 and 7-by-3 is the expression of the fact that each row in the left matrix is conformable for multiplication with each column in the right matrix. In general, two matrices are said to be conformable for multiplication if the number of columns in the left matrix equals the number of rows in the right matrix. We can summarize this by saying that a p by q matrix on the left multiplied by a q by r matrix on the right gives a p by r matrix.

As an example, let's take the same 3-by-2 matrix on the right as before:

$$R^{\sim} = \begin{bmatrix} 1 & 3 \\ 2 & -1 \\ 4 & 2 \end{bmatrix}$$

But on the left, let's take not just one row, but a 2-by-3 matrix L~:

$$\begin{bmatrix} 3 & 2 & 5 \\ 4 & -1 & 6 \end{bmatrix}$$

The product of the first row of the left matrix and the right matrix R~ is something we worked out before as:

$$[\quad 27 \quad 17 \quad]$$

You might like to verify that multiplying the second row of the left matrix and the right matrix leads to a second row:

$$[\quad 26 \quad 25 \quad]$$

So the result of the multiplication is the 2-by-2 matrix:

$$\begin{bmatrix} 27 & 17 \\ 26 & 25 \end{bmatrix}$$

In the previous discussion, we talked above about the "matrix on the left" and the "matrix on the right" at various stages. The reason is that the left or right position of each matrix is significant. In multiplication with single numbers, 3 times 2 is the same as 2 times 3, i.e., interchanging the position of the numbers does not make a difference. In the case of matrices, generally it does make a difference. Interchanging them might make multiplication impossible, and even if possible it might not give the same result.

As an example of impossibility, we can multiply a 3-by-7 matrix on the left by a 7-by-4 matrix on the right. As we saw previously, the result would be a 3-by-4 matrix. But if we interchange their positions, we cannot multiply a 7-by-4 matrix on the left by a 3-by-7 matrix on the right because each row on the left has 4 elements, but each column on the right has only 3 elements.

As an example of different results, a 4-by-3 matrix on the left multiplied by a 3-by-4 matrix on the right will give a 4-by-4 matrix. If we interchange their positions, they can be multiplied, but the result will be a 3-by-3 matrix, which has 9 numbers in it. Clearly, this is different from a 4-by-4 matrix with 16 numbers in it. Sometimes multiplication might be possible and also lead to the same dimensions for the result when we interchange the positions. For example, if we have two 2-by-2

matrices, we can multiply them to get a 2-by-2 matrix as the result, whichever one we put on the left. But the results will not generally be the same, though in some cases they might be the same. For example, you might like to multiply the following two matrices and verify that, depending on which one is on the left, you get two different results.

$$\begin{bmatrix} 4 & 5 \\ 2 & 3 \end{bmatrix}$$

times

$$\begin{bmatrix} 1 & -2 \\ 7 & 1 \end{bmatrix}$$

gives the result:

$$\begin{bmatrix} 39 & -3 \\ 23 & -1 \end{bmatrix}$$

On the other hand,

$$\begin{bmatrix} 1 & -2 \\ 7 & 1 \end{bmatrix}$$

times

$$\begin{bmatrix} 4 & 5 \\ 2 & 3 \end{bmatrix}$$

gives the result:

$$\begin{bmatrix} 0 & -1 \\ 30 & 38 \end{bmatrix}$$

This is described by saying that, in general, matrix multiplication is not *commutative* (i.e., we cannot interchange the left and right positions of the two matrices and get the same result), whereas multiplication of ordinary numbers is always commutative. As another example, we saw that multiplying the 1-by-3 matrix or row [1 2 4] by the 3-by-1 matrix or column [3 2 5] gives the number 27. In line with what we saw about the relationship between the dimensions of the matrices, the multiplication of a 1-by-3 matrix on the left and a 3-by-1 matrix on the right should give us a 1-by-1 matrix, and the single number 27 we got can formally be regarded as a matrix of 1 row and 1 column.

Suppose we interchange their left and right positions; are they conformable for multiplication? The matrix on the left is now 3 by 1, and that on the right is 1 by 3. So we have satisfied the requirement that the left matrix has as many columns as the right matrix has rows. But since each row of the left matrix generates a row in the product, and there would be as many columns in the product as there are in the right matrix, the product would be a 3-by-3 matrix. You might like to verify that the product is in fact:

$$\begin{bmatrix} 3 \\ 2 \\ 5 \end{bmatrix}$$

times

$$\begin{bmatrix} 1 & 2 & 4 \end{bmatrix}$$

$$=$$

$$\begin{bmatrix} 3 & 6 & 12 \\ 2 & 4 & 8 \\ 5 & 10 & 20 \end{bmatrix}$$

Neural network operations in terms of matrices

With this overview of matrices, let's look at how the operations of neural networks can be very conveniently and naturally expressed in terms of matrix operations. We saw that the basic operation of a neuron is to form a weighted sum of the inputs. As mentioned earlier, we can write:

$$\text{net input} = X^{\sim} \text{ times } w^{\sim}$$

where the "times" is the matrix multiplication discussed previously, $X^{\sim}$ is the input vector:

$$[\ X1 \ \ X2 \ \ X3 \ \ldots \ ]$$

and $w^{\sim}$ is the weight vector:

$$\begin{bmatrix} w1 \\ w2 \\ . \\ . \end{bmatrix}$$

Now, instead of looking at a single neuron, let's look at the first processing layer of neurons in a feedforward network. We know that each of the inputs is connected to each of the neurons in the processing layer by a certain weight. We know that we have 9 weights involved if, as in Fig. A-1, we have three input units, unit_1, unit_2 and unit_3 with inputs $X1$, $X2$, and $X3$, and three units in the first processing layer, unit_4 unit_5 and unit_6. We have:

➤ $w14$, $w15m$ and $w16$ connecting input 1 to the three neurons in the processing layer.

➤ $w24$, $w25$, and $w26$ connecting input 2 to the three neurons.

➤ $w34$, $w35$, and $w36$ connecting input 3 to the three neurons.

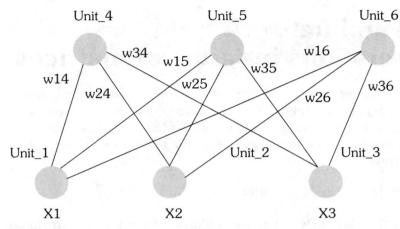

Units 1, 2, and 3 in the input layer are connected to units 4, 5, and 6 in the first processing layer, with weights w14, w15, w16 . . .

If we set up these 9 weights as a matrix and call it:

$$W^\sim = \begin{bmatrix} w14 & w15 & w16 \\ w24 & w25 & w26 \\ w34 & w35 & w36 \end{bmatrix}$$

and place it on the right, and we place the input matrix (row vector) [X1 X2 X3] = X~ on the left, we see that the multiplication gives us a row in which the first element is X1 * w14 + X2 * w24 + X3 * w34, which is the net input to unit 4 in the first processing layer. Similarly, the second and third elements in the product give us the net inputs to units 5 and 6.

So we can succinctly express the ordered list of inputs to the three units in the first processing layer as: X~ times W~. Since X~ is a 1-by-3 row, and W~ is a 3-by-3 matrix, the product is a 1-by-3 row of three net inputs to unit_4, unit_5 and unit_6. Suppose the transfer functions

of these three neurons operate on these net inputs to produce outputs that we can designate as O4, O5 and O6. If the next layer has, say, 4 units, we need a matrix of dimensions 3 by 4, one row for each of the processing units in the first layer, and in each row four weights for connections to each of the units in the second processing layer. Once again, multiplying the row [O4 O5 O6] by this matrix will give us a row of 4 net inputs to the 4 units in the second layer . . . and so on, layer by layer.

⇨ Why use matrices?

We can see from the previous discussion that matrix notation is a short and elegant way of expressing in condensed form the various operations that we had earlier considered in a piece-by-piece fashion. But this useful advantage of being able to express concisely the calculations involved is by no means the major or most important reason for using matrices. Ever since the concept of matrices was introduced by the British mathematician Cayley in the 19th century, matrices have been extensively investigated and applied in a vast number of fields. As a result, a powerful body of results is available about the application of matrices, their implicit properties, and the conclusions that emerge as a result of their application. The recognition that neural networks essentially are based on matrix transformations allows the whole body of knowledge about matrix algebra to be brought into play, without having to start from scratch in investigating the consequences of the transformations involved. A good illustration of this would be to consider Hopfield nets.

In our discussion of Hopfield nets, we saw that Hopfield postulated that the weights connecting unit i to unit j is the same as the weight connecting unit j to unit i. That is, the connections are symmetrical. He also postulated that the weight connecting each unit to itself is 0.

Now, let's see what this means in the language of matrix algebra. If we consider the matrix of connections in a small network with 4 units, the matrix of weights would be:

$$\begin{bmatrix} 0 & w12 & w13 & w14 \\ w12 & 0 & w23 & w24 \\ w13 & w23 & 0 & w34 \\ w14 & w24 & w34 & 0 \end{bmatrix}$$

The diagonal elements would all be 0. The weights below the diagonal would match those above because of symmetry.

The general theory of matrices has extensively investigated the properties of symmetric matrices, and matrices with 0s on the diagonal, in connection with various other applications. So all of this existing knowledge can be used in connection with Hopfield nets. This introduction is meant only to indicate the relationship between matrix algebra and neural networks, so we will not go into too much further detail. There are many excellent books on matrix algebra, or linear algebra as it alternatively is called. As one of the most readable books, we recommend W. W. Sawyer's *An Engineering Approach to Linear Algebra* (Cambridge University Press, 1972). However, for the sake of completeness, and also for the purposes of the next appendix, let's conclude this chapter by looking at some key properties of matrices.

We defined matrix multiplication previously in terms of the following steps: multiply row 1 of the left matrix L~ by the right matrix R~, column by column, to get the first row of the product. Then repeat the procedure with row 2, row 3 . . . of L~ to get the successive rows of the product. Alternatively, it is possible to multiply the first column of R~ by each row of L~ in turn, to get the first column of the product, and then repeat the procedure with successive columns of the product. The result would be the same in either case.

A special kind of matrix that has a central role is called the *identity matrix*. It is a square matrix; it has the same number of rows and columns, and it has 0s everywhere except on the *principal diagonal*,

i.e., on the diagonal from the top left corner to the bottom right corner. For example, the 3-by-3 identity matrix is:

$$I(3)^\sim = \begin{bmatrix} 1 & 0 & 0 \\ 0 & 1 & 0 \\ 0 & 0 & 1 \end{bmatrix}$$

We know that, because this has three rows, it can be the left multiplier of any right matrix with 3 columns, e.g.:

$$M^\sim = \begin{bmatrix} 4 & 2 \\ 7 & -6 \\ 8 & 11 \end{bmatrix}$$

This multiplication gives us back the matrix R$^\sim$, hence the name "identity." We can think of it as analogous to multiplying a single number by 1.

For multiplying the same matrix by another matrix on the right, we know that it needs to have two rows for conformability for multiplication. If we take the same matrix M$^\sim$ on the left and multiply it by the identity matrix:

$$\begin{bmatrix} 1 & 0 \\ 0 & 1 \end{bmatrix}$$

on the right, the result again preserves the identity of M$^\sim$. Also, if we have a square matrix, let's say dimensions 4 by 4, then the identity matrix for multiplication from the left or from the right would be I(4)$^\sim$. So, for a square matrix, multiplication with the identity matrix would be commutative.

We had mentioned addition, subtraction, and multiplication of matrices. What about division? The concept of an identity matrix leads us to the analog of division for numbers. First, let's look more closely

at what is meant by dividing one number by another, say dividing 3 by 5. We can think of it as really the inverse operation to multiplication: we are trying to find an answer a such that $5 * a = 3$. Now, if we multiply both sides of this equation by the reciprocal of 5, i.e., $\frac{1}{5}$, we get on the left side:

$$\frac{1}{5} * 5 * a = 1 * a$$

and on the right side:

$$\frac{1}{5} * 3 = \frac{3}{5}$$

So we might say that division by 5 is the same as multiplication by the reciprocal of 5, i.e., $\frac{1}{5}$.

By thinking of division by a number as equivalent to multiplication by the reciprocal of that number, we can develop an analogous operation for matrices. This is generally defined only for square matrices, though there are some extensions to nonsquare matrices in which the numbers of rows and columns are not equal.

We can say that if we want to solve the equation:

$$R\text{~} \text{ times } A\text{~} = B\text{~}$$

where A~ and B~ are given square matrices, say, of dimensions 4 by 4, analogous to the numbers 5 and 3 in the division of numbers in the example above, and R~ is the result we want, then "dividing" B~ by A~ would be equivalent to multiplying B~ by the "reciprocal" of A~. We saw that the identity matrix plays the same role as 1 in ordinary arithmetic, so just as a number times its reciprocal equals 1, we need to find a matrix such that A~ times this matrix equals an identity matrix. Also, if A~ and B~ are square matrices of dimensions 4 by 4, we can see that R~ has to be 4 by 4, and so does the "reciprocal." In the case of matrices, the analog of reciprocal is called the *inverse* of the matrix. Let's call it inv(A~).

So, if there is a matrix inv(A~) such that:

$$A\text{~} * \text{inv}(A\text{~}) = I(4)\text{~}$$

then we see that by multiplying both sides of the equation R~ * A~ = B~ by inv(R~) on the right, we would get:

$$R~ * A~ * inv(A~) = B~ * inv(A~)$$

And since A~ * inv(A~) is the identity matrix I(4)~, and since R~ * I(4)~ = R~ (property of an identity matrix), we can find the answer to be:

$$R~ = B~ * inv(A~)$$

Not all square matrices would have an inverse, but as an illustration, consider the following 2-by-2 matrix P~:

$$P~ = \begin{bmatrix} 2 & 3 \\ 1 & 4 \end{bmatrix}$$

You might like to take the matrix:

$$Q~ = \begin{bmatrix} 0.8 & -0.6 \\ -0.2 & 0.4 \end{bmatrix}$$

and verify by matrix multiplication that P~ * Q~ gives the result:

$$\begin{bmatrix} 1 & 0 \\ 0 & 1 \end{bmatrix}$$

So, Q~ is in fact the inverse of P~~.

An inverse, when it is there, has the property that multiplying a matrix by its inverse from the left or from the right gives the identity matrix as the result, i.e., multiplication of a matrix by its inverse is commutative. You might like to verify that Q~ * P~ gives I(2)~ in the previous example. The definition of multiplication we have given previously is the one most useful for most applications. But there is an alternative method of forming a product, called the direct product of matrices, in which only two matrices of the same

dimensions can be multiplied, and each element in the product is the product of the elements in the same row and column position (i.e., this "product" is similar to the operations used in addition and multiplication).

There are special techniques and computer programs for finding inverses of matrices, since they have a vast variety of applications. As an illustration of one of the earliest and also one of the most widespread uses, let's consider their application to solving simultaneous equations.

Suppose we have the pair of equations:

$$2x + 1y = 12$$

$$3x + 4y = 13$$

The nonmatrix way of solving such equations would be to "eliminate variables" by, say, multiplying the first equation by 3 and the second equation by 2 to get:

$$6x + 3y = 36$$

$$6x + 8y = 26$$

Subtraction would give $-5y = 10$ or $y = -2$, and substituting this in either equation would give:

$$x = 7$$

From a matrix point of view, you could think of the set of equations as:

$$[\; x \;\; y \;] * \begin{bmatrix} 2 & 3 \\ 1 & 4 \end{bmatrix} = [\; 12 \;\; 13 \;]$$

$$\text{or } [\; x \;\; y \;] * M^\sim = [\; 12 \;\; 13 \;]$$

where we denote by $M^\sim$ the matrix:

$$\begin{bmatrix} 2 & 3 \\ 1 & 4 \end{bmatrix}$$

since the multiplication of the row and matrix on the left do give the same equations:

$$2x + 1y$$

and

$$3x + 4y$$

In terms of what we saw about inverses, the solution [x y] we are looking for is therefore:

$$[\ 12\ \ 13\ ] * \text{inv}(M^\sim)$$

We had at an earlier stage found inv(M~) to be:

$$\begin{bmatrix} 0.8 & -0.6 \\ -0.2 & 0.4 \end{bmatrix}$$

You might like to verify that this multiplication does lead to the result:

$$[\ x\ \ y\ ] = [\ 7\ \ -2\ ]$$

which is the result we got by "elimination of variables."

Of course, the real power of the method arises in sets of equations with many more variables, where the ability to get matrices and carry out matrix multiplication conveniently becomes very handy indeed. Instead of writing the pair of equations in matrix form as:

$$[\ x\ \ y\ ] * \begin{bmatrix} 2 & 3 \\ 1 & 4 \end{bmatrix} = [\ 12\ \ 13\ ]$$

we could also have written it as;

$$\begin{bmatrix} 2 & 1 \\ 3 & 4 \end{bmatrix} * \begin{bmatrix} x \\ y \end{bmatrix} = \begin{bmatrix} 12 \\ 13 \end{bmatrix}$$

We can see that the matrix we have on the left is the transpose of the matrix M~ we had before. Let's call it N~~, so that the equation is now:

$$N\text{~} * \begin{bmatrix} x \\ y \end{bmatrix} = \begin{bmatrix} 12 \\ 13 \end{bmatrix}$$

By the same kind of argument as before, if we can find the inverse of N, we can solve the equation and get:

$$\begin{bmatrix} x \\ y \end{bmatrix} = inv(N\text{~}) * \begin{bmatrix} 12 \\ 13 \end{bmatrix}$$

You might like to verify, by multiplying N~ and the matrix below to get I(2)~, that it is the inverse of N~:

$$\begin{bmatrix} 0.8 & -0.2 \\ -0.6 & 0.4 \end{bmatrix}$$

Further, multiplying this by:

$$\begin{bmatrix} 12 \\ 13 \end{bmatrix}$$

does give:

$$\begin{bmatrix} x \\ y \end{bmatrix} = \begin{bmatrix} 7 \\ -2 \end{bmatrix}$$

Notice also that the inverse of the transpose of M~ is the same as the transpose of the inverse of M~. This is a general result that can be proven to be true in all cases. Many standard programs are available for finding the inverse of a given square matrix, which will find the inverse if one exists or indicate that the matrix does not have an inverse.

 Matrices and Spaces

Finally, let's look at another way of considering matrices that comes in useful in a number of applications. Let's consider the following matrix product:

$$\text{point A} * \text{M}^\sim = \text{point B}$$

$$[\ 3 \ \ 4 \ ] * \begin{bmatrix} 1 & 3 \\ 2 & -1 \end{bmatrix} = [\ 11 \ \ 5 \ ]$$

We can say that the effect of the multiplication by the matrix M~ is to move the point A with coordinates 3, 4 to a different position B with coordinates 11, 5 as in Fig. A-2.

What if the matrix is 2 by 3 instead of 2 by 2? We know the result would be a row of 3 elements, and we could say that the point in two-dimensional space has now been projected into three dimensions. Similarly, a point in three-dimensional space, multiplied by a 3-by-2 matrix, would lead to a new point in two-dimensional space, and so on. By a metaphorical use of the word "space" to denote an ordered list of numbers, we can think of any matrix as essentially moving a point from a space of 2, 3, 4 . . . or any number of dimensions (the number of elements in the row on the left) to a space of 2, 3, 4 . . . dimensions (the number of columns in the matrix, since the multiplication of a row vector by a matrix conformable for multiplication will produce a row with as many elements as there are columns in the matrix).

Figure A-2

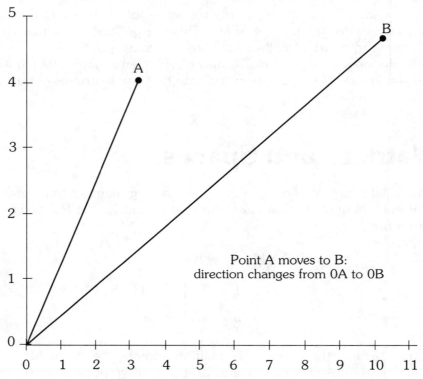

Multiplication by matrix moves point A to point B.

The importance of matrices for the study of neural networks is among other things indicated by the fact that the seminal book *Parallel Distributed Processing* by Rumelhart and McClelland includes a special section on matrix algebra, as chapter 9 of volume 1 (An Introduction to Linear Algebra for Parallel Distributed Processing by M. I. Jordan).

B

Neural networks
and statistical analysis

WE saw in the appendix on matrices that the field of neural networks, as it evolved, benefitted from the conceptual connections between neural networks and the algebra of matrices. The body of knowledge developed over many years could be brought to play in the new field. In exactly the same way, a close relationship exists between neural networks and the techniques of statistical analysis, especially *multivariate statistical analysis*, which involves many variables.

In his introduction to *Neurocomputing 2: Directions for Research*, Dr. James Anderson, one of the leading researchers in the field of neural networks has this to say: "It has become clear in the past couple of years that some older techniques from pattern recognition and statistics are similar to some of the ideas developed for neural networks." He mentions in particular that an idea from statistics that is coming to greater and greater prominence in neural networks is the multivariate statistical theory of *principal components*.

This appendix aims to give readers an overview of multivariate statistical theory and in particular principal components. To make the introduction self-contained, we start with a review of basic statistical concepts and then go to a discussion of multivariate statistical analysis and principal components. We hope the introduction will be helpful to readers who would like to study further the work being done regarding the relationship between neural networks and statistics.

→ Basic statistical concepts

Subject to some qualifications, you can think of statistical analysis as essentially concerned with drawing reliable conclusions from a study of samples. For example, public opinion polls collect information from a sample of persons and on that basis give estimates about the opinions of all people in the country. Similarly, measurements of income, poverty, and similar socioeconomic *variables* are made using suitable samples and, on that basis, estimates are made and conclusions drawn about the whole *population* from which the sample was drawn. (In statistics, the word "population" is used to refer not only to people, but also to any collection of objects that is the subject of study. For example, if a sample of, say, 50 electronic components from a production line are taken and measurements made, this sample is said to be a sample of the "population" of all components being produced in that production process.) There are, of course, many finer points involved in making such estimates. Most important, how can you ensure that the sample is a representative sample, so that it "truly represents" the whole collection about which you are going to draw conclusions? And what is the margin of error in making estimates using a sample rather than making measurements of the whole collection?

Briefly, we might say that to make sure we have a representative sample, usually (but not always) a *random sample* is drawn. The process of drawing a sample is designed so that each of the theoretically possible samples that can be drawn has an equal chance or probability of being drawn. Secondly, the margin of error in estimates made from samples can be theoretically calculated using advanced statistical analysis. For our purposes, let's focus on the basic processes involved in making measurements and drawing conclusions.

 # The mean and variance of a variable

In special cases, you would deal with variables or attributes that have only two possible values, yes or no, as in taking a poll where opinions are collected about whether the person is for or against something. These are called *binary variables*. But more typically, measurements that lead to real numbers are involved, as in measuring income, age, weight, height, and so on. Typically, you would also collect data about a number of variables, i.e., *multivariate* data, rather than about a single variable (*univariate* data). But we will start by reviewing some concepts relating to single variables, and then we will extend the discussion to multivariate data. Ultimately, univariate data for each of the variables combines to constitute multivariate data. Two *derived measurements* or *constructs* that come out of the data from a sample are of key importance in statistical analysis. The first is the *mean* or *average* value.

⇨ Mean or average of a sample

This is a familiar concept: if we measure the income of a sample of ten people, we add up all the measurements and divide them by 10. In general, for a sample of size n, i.e., a sample with n units in it, we divide the sum by n. We can view the calculation of the mean in terms of the concepts of vectors and matrices by saying that if the measurements we have made are $V(1), V(2), V(3) \ldots V(n)$, then the mean is the product of a row vector and a column vector as follows:

$$[\ V(1) \ \ V(2) \ \ V(3) \ldots \ . \ V(n) \ ] * \begin{bmatrix} 1/n \\ 1/n \\ 1/n \\ 1/n \end{bmatrix}$$

Alternatively, we can think of the sum of the variables as the product:

$$[\ V(1) \ \ V(2) \ldots \ . \ . \ ] * \begin{bmatrix} 1 \\ 1 \\ . \end{bmatrix}$$

This product of a 1-by-n row and a n-by-1 column is a 1-by-1 matrix or single number, and the mean is $1/n$ times this number. Each of the values of the variable is called one *observation*.

In other words, the mean is a weighted sum just like the weighted sums we saw earlier, with the weights all equal and equal to $1/n$. Similarly, the sum of the values is a weighted sum, with all the weights equal to 1. The standard notation for the mean is to write the variable symbol with a bar on top: here it will be represented in the form V_bar, for mean of variable V.

The various values would usually not be all exactly equal to the average; some would be higher and some lower. The mean is called a measure of *central tendency*, since it broadly indicates a central or representative value for all the units in the sample.

⇨ The variance of a variable

As the name *variance* suggests, this is a way of measuring the variability in the values. The precise definition of variance starts with the concept of the extent to which a value is different from the mean. This is called the *deviation from the mean*. For example, if we have collected data for three days on the number of accidents that happened that day, and the numbers are 10, 8, and 15, we have a sample of three measurements or *observations*, with a mean of (10 + 8 + 15)/3 = 11. The deviations of the three values are (10 −11), (8 −11) and (15 −11), i.e., −1, −3, and +4. In general, the deviations would be (V(1) − V_bar), (V(2) − V_bar). It is customary to use the symbol with lowercase to represent the deviations, i.e., the deviations are $v(1)$, $v(2)$ . . . When we convert measurements of the values into deviations, these have the property that the sum of the deviations is 0, and this makes further analysis more convenient. One way we can see why the deviations sum to 0 is by looking at the definition of V_bar in matrix form as given previously:

Sum of deviations = V(1) − V_bar + V(2) − V_bar . . .

= V(1) + V(2) . . . − n * V_bar, since V_bar occurs n times.

$$= V(1) + V(2) \ldots - n * [\,[V(1) \quad V(2) .. \;]\,] * \begin{bmatrix} 1/n \\ 1/n \\ . \\ . \end{bmatrix}$$

$$= V(1) + V(2) \ldots - [\,[\, n*V(1)\ \ n*V(2) \ldots \ldots\,]\,] * \begin{bmatrix} 1/n \\ 1/n \\ . \\ . \end{bmatrix}$$

which leads to

$$V(1) + V(2) \ldots - (\, V(1) + V(2) + \ldots\,)$$

$$= 0$$

A deviation can be positive, i.e., the value is greater than the mean, or the deviation can be negative, i.e., the value is less than the mean. When we want to measure the variability in the values, it seems reasonable to say that both positive and negative deviations should be taken into account and not allowed to cancel each other out. To take this into account, the measure of variability, the variance, is calculated by taking the *squares of the deviations* and adding them up, so that a positive deviation of say, 2, and a negative deviation of −2 are both regarded as contributing equally to the variability. This sum is then divided by the number of measurements or observations minus one. The result is called the estimate of the variance of the whole collection of measurements that we are studying using a sample. The alternative name for variance makes it explicit what it is about: *mean squared deviation*.

(If measurements are available for the whole collection of objects we are studying, then the variance would be measured as the sum of squares of deviations divided by the number of observations, hence giving the mean of the squared deviations. However, typically only a sample would have been used, and theoretically it can be proven that a better estimate of the variance of the whole set can be obtained by dividing the sum of squares of deviations in the sample by the sample size minus 1.) We could say the values of the squared deviations are treated as a new *derived variable* and the variance of the original variable is defined to be the mean of this derived variable. In the previous example, the estimate of the variance is:

((–1) squared + (–3) squared + (+4) squared) / (3 – 1)

From the definition, we can see that the variance can never be a negative number, and the lowest possible value it can have is 0. This will happen only if all the deviations are 0, which means all the values are the same and so the mean is the same as each of the values. A further derived variable is the positive square root of the variance, and this is called the *standard deviation*.

It turns out that the variance (and standard deviation), as defined previously, have some other interesting properties. One of the most general is what is known as Chebychev's inequality. This says that for any variable whatever, the chances or probability of getting any values of the variable that deviate by k or more standard deviations from the mean (i.e., that lie at or beyond the mean plus or minus k times the standard deviation, where k is some positive number greater than 1) is less than or equal to 1 divided by k squared. For example, the chances that for any variable a randomly selected observation will lie 5 or more standard deviations from the mean is not more than $\frac{1}{5}$ squared, or 4%.

Standardized value of a variable

In addition to converting the values into deviations, one other transformation or adjustment is usually made. This is to divide the value of the deviation by the standard deviation. The rationale for this is the following: We want the variance to be a general measure of variability between the different values, and we would like to have a measurement that does not depend on the scale used. If we measure lengths in feet, we would get one value for the variance, and if we measured it in inches, we would get 144 times the value. (Each measurement, and the mean, would be 12 times as much, and so would be the deviations, so the squared deviations would become 12 squared or 144 times as much.) To avoid this effect, the values of the deviations are divided by the standard deviation, to give what are called *standardized values*.

When such standardization is made, the scale we use does not matter because, in the previous example, each deviation would go up 12

times, and so would the standard deviation, so the standardized value would remain the same. We can also see that when we standardize different variables with different variances, all of them will have a variance of 1. However, this does not mean that they have their values distributed at different values in the same way. The same squared deviation of 1 could arise from very different patterns of distributions of the values, or different *frequency distributions*. But the comparison of how they are spread out or are distributed with regard to their mean value of 0 is more meaningful when they all have a standardized variance of 1.

 # Extension to multivariate statistics

Multivariate statistics is concerned with making measurements of more than one variable or attribute for each of the units we are concerned with, and with studying the relationship between these variables. For instance, a study might be concerned with collecting data on three variables, unemployment rate, inflation, and per-capita income for a number of countries. In that case, there is the question of the mean and variance of each of the variables, and the question of the relationship between the variables. To put it another way, how is their variability connected? Do they seem to increase together, or is there a pattern of one increasing when another or others decrease, and so on?

The measurement of the variability of each variable separately and of the relationships between them are again very conveniently studied by using matrix notation. Let's consider an example with only three variables. When we were dealing with a single variable, we called it V and called the different values or observations $V(1)$, $V(2)$, $V(3)$ . . . etc. When we have more than one variable, the convention about naming them is as follows: We call the first, second, third . . . variable as $V(*,1)$, $V(*,2)$, and $V(*,3)$.

To denote successive values or observations of a variable, we use the place where the "*" is shown in parentheses above to indicate the number of the observation. So, if we have ten values or observations of the first variable, or $V(*,1)$, we designate them as: $V(1,1)$, $V(2,1)$, $V(3,1)$, $V(4,1)$ . . . $V(10,1)$ . . . In other words, two *indices* are used between parentheses, with the first index denoting the observation number and the second index the variable number. So the successive observations of the second variable, $V(*,2)$ would be: $V(1,2)$, $V(2,2)$, $V(3,2)$ . . . $V(10,2)$ . . . and so on. (You might find that some books reverse the indices and use the first index for the variable number and the second index for the observation number, i.e., the first variable is called $V(1,*)$ and the successive observations of this variable are designated as $V(1,1)$, $V(1,2)$, $V(1,3)$ . . . It does not matter which convention is used so long as it is consistently used for all the variables.)

In our example of 10 observations of three variables, let's put the 10 observations of the first variable in the first column of a matrix, the second variable in the second column, and the third variable in the third column as follows:

$$\begin{bmatrix} V(1,1) & V(1,2) & V(1,3) \\ V(2,1) & V(2,2) & V(2,3) \\ V(3,1) & V(3,2) & V(3,3) \\ & \cdots & \\ V(10,1) & V(10,2) & V(10,3) \end{bmatrix}$$

As an alternative to thinking of the 10 observations of each variable being in one column, we can also think of each row as representing one list of observations for all the variables, e.g., row 8 has $V(8,1)$, $V(8,2)$, and $V(8,3)$, which we can think of as the vector of values for the eight observation of all three variables. We can calculate the mean of each variable separately by taking the columns one at time, convert the values into deviations, and setting up a new matrix:

$$\begin{bmatrix} v(1,1) & v(1,2) & v(1,3) \\ v(2,1) & v(2,2) & v(2,3) \\ & \cdots & \\ & \cdots & \\ v(10,1) & v(10,2) & v(10,3) \end{bmatrix}$$

As before, lowercase v is used to denote that we are using deviations. Let's call this matrix of deviations D~. In general, it will have as many rows as there are observations, and as many columns as there are variables.

Many of the important concepts of multivariate statistical analysis are captured by a matrix that is formed by multiplying this matrix of deviations D~ from the left, using its transpose, transp(D~):

transp(D~) * D~ =

$$
\begin{bmatrix}
v(1,1) & v(2,1) & v(3,1) & \ldots & v(10,1) \\
v(1,2) & v(2,2) & v(3,2) & \ldots & v(10,2) \\
v(1,3) & v(2,3) & v(3,3) & \ldots & v(10,3)
\end{bmatrix}
$$

*

$$
\begin{bmatrix}
v(1,1) & v(1,2) & v(1,3) \\
v(2,1) & v(2,2) & v(2,3) \\
& \ldots & \\
v(10,1) & v(10,2) & v(10,3)
\end{bmatrix}
$$

We know that the product of the 3-by-10 matrix transp(D~) and the 10-by-3 matrix D~ will produce a 3-by-3 square matrix. In general, the product will be a square matrix with its rows and columns equal to the number of variables, in this case, 3. Let's first consider what will appear on the *principal diagonal of the product*, i.e., in row 1, column 1; row 2, column 2; and row 3, column 3. By the rule for multiplying matrices, the element in the first row and first column is calculated by multiplying the first row of transp(D~) and the first column of D~:

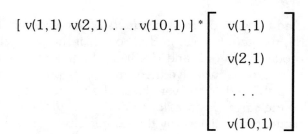

We see that this is the sum of the squares of the deviations $v(1,1)$, $v(2,1)$ . . . of the variable $V(*,1)$. In other words, we can get the variance of $V(*,1)$ by dividing this sum by (number of elements in sample − 1), in this case, $10 - 1 = 9$. In the same way, the next diagonal element is formed by multiplying row 2 of transp(D~) by column 2 of D~, and this gives us the sum of squares of deviations of $V(*,2)$ . . . In general, the elements on the principal diagonal give us the estimates of the variances of the variables. If instead of just using the deviations, we also standardize them, then all the elements on the principal diagonal will become 1.

Now, let's consider the off-diagonal elements. We know that to get the element in column 2 of the first row, we would multiply row 1 of transp(D~) by the second column of D~:

$$[(v1,1)\ v(2,1)\ v(3,1)\ .\ .\ .\ ] * \begin{bmatrix} v(1,2) \\ v(2,2) \\ .\ .\ . \end{bmatrix}$$

This sum is:

$$v(1,1) * v(1,2) +$$

$$v(2,1) * v(2,2) +$$

$$.\ .\ .$$

$$v(10,1) * v(10,2)$$

This sum is called the *sum of cross-products* of variables $V(*,1)$ and $V(*,2)$. Similarly, the item in column 3 of row 1 of the product gives the sum of cross-products of $V(*,1)$ and $V(*,3)$ . . . In general, the item in row p column q of the product will give the sum of crossproducts of $V(*,p)$ and $V(*,q)$, the "p th" and "q th" variables. The product of transp(D˜) and D˜ is called the *variance-covariance matrix* or *dispersion matrix* when all the elements are divided by the sample size, minus 1.

The fact that the covariance is formed by multiplying the deviations of the two variables $V(*,1)$ and $V(*,2)$ for each observation 1, 2, . . . 10 tells us something about how they tend to be associated or vary together. Suppose they vary together, so that whenever $v(*,1)$ is positive, i.e., showing that the variable $V(*,1)$ is above average, $v(*,2)$ is also positive, showing that $V(*,2)$ is also average for that observation, and whenever one deviation is negative, the other is also negative. Every term in the sum of cross-products will be positive, and we will get a high positive value for the sum.

Suppose they always vary in opposite directions, i.e., whenever the deviation of one variable is positive, the deviation of the other is negative, and vice-versa. Then every term in the sum of cross-products will be negative and we'll get a very negative value for the sum.

Suppose they are essentially independent of each other, i.e., when $v(*,1)$ is above average, $v(*,2)$ might be above or below average, and vice-versa. We see that some of the terms would be positive and some negative, and the sum is likely to be low or close to 0. So, the value of the covariance of two variances of two variables tells us whether they tend to vary together, in opposite directions, or are essentially independent.

In the previous example, we can see that the element in row 2 and column 1 of the product will be calculated by multiplying the second row of transp(D˜) by the first column of (D˜ to give:

$$v(1,2) * v(1,1) \quad v(2,2) * v(2,1) \ . \ . \ .$$

It is again the sum of cross-products of $V(*,1)$ and $V(*,2)$. In the same way, the element in row p and column q will always be the same as the element in row q and column p, so the variance-covariance matrix is *symmetrical*: if we transpose the rows and columns, the matrix will not change.

Instead of using the deviations, if we use the standardized deviations in setting up the matrix D~, the resulting product is called the *correlation matrix*. The variances or elements along the principal diagonal will all become 1. The off-diagonal elements are called the *correlation coefficients*. The element in, say, row 4, column 5 is called the correlation coefficient of variables $V(*,4)$ and $V(*,5)$, and, as we saw, because of the symmetry of the matrix, the same value will appear in row 5 column 4. The correlation coefficients can be proven to have the following characteristics:

➤ They are always between +1 and −1.

➤ If two variables have a perfectly linear relationship, (i.e., a graph plotting one of the variables on the horizontal axis and the other on the vertical axis is a sloping straight line) the correlation coefficient will be +1 or −1, depending on whether the line is upward sloping or downward sloping.

➤ If the variables are independent of each other, the correlation coefficient will be 0. (However, the converse is not true. If the correlation coefficient is 0, they are not necessarily independent of each other. All it means is they do not have a linear relationship.)

⇨ Principal component analysis

This statistical technique for analysis of multivariate data was developed in 1901 by Karl Pearson and developed further by Harold Hotelling in the 1930s. The essence of the technique can be described as follows: Suppose we have a number of variables $V(*,1)$, $V(*,2)$ . . . and we have the data matrix for these variables, expressed in standardized form as:

$$D~ =$$

$$\begin{bmatrix} v(1,1) & v(1,2) & v(1,3) & \cdots \\ v(2,1) & v(2,2) & v(2,3) & \cdots \\ & \cdots & & \end{bmatrix}$$

The different values of each variable are in each of the columns, and the list or vector of values of all the variables is in a different row for each observation.

We saw that a correlation matrix can be derived from this data matrix by multiplying transp(D~) ∗ D~, and this matrix will have 1 along the principal diagonal and the correlation coefficients off the diagonal. Let's call the correlation matrix C~.

If the correlations are not 0, we know that the variables are not linearly independent. The total variance of the variables considered as a collection is n, where n is the number of variables we have, since each has a variance of 1. We can also think of the total variance as the sum of the numbers in the principal diagonal of the correlation matrix.

Principal components analysis does the following with data of this kind: It replaces the original set of n variables, $v(*,1)$, $v(*,2)$ . . . $v(*,n)$ with a set of n *derived variables*, i.e., variables whose values are derived from the values of the original variables. These derived variables are called the *principal components*. Let's represent them as $pc(*,1)$, $pc(*,2)$ . . . $pc(*,n)$. Since one value of each principal component is derived for each observation of the original variables, each principal component will also have as many values or observations as each of the original variables has.

Each principal component is derived as a *weighted sum* or *linear combination* of the values of the original variables:

$$pc(1,1) = a1 * v(1,1) + a2 * v(1,2) + a3 * v(1,3) . .$$

$$pc(1,2) = b1 * v(1,1) + b2 * v(1,2) + b3 * v(1,3) . .$$

$$pc(1,3) = c1 * v(1,1) + c2 * v(1,2) + c3 * v(1,3) . .$$

$$pc(2,1) = a1 * v(2,1) + a2 * v(2,2) + a3 * v(2,3) . .$$

$$pc(2,2) = b1 * v(2,1) + b2 * v(2,2) + b3 * v(2,3) . .$$

$$pc(2,3) = c1 * v(2,1) + c2 * v(2,2) + c3 * v(2,3) . .$$

. . . .

If we call the data matrix for the principal components P~, we can represent the derivation of the values of the principal components as:

$$
P\sim = \begin{bmatrix} pc(1,1) & pc(1,2) & \ldots & pc(1,n) \\ pc(2,1) & pc(2,2) & \ldots & pc(2,n) \\ \ldots \\ pc(m,1) & pc(m,2) & & pc(m,n) \end{bmatrix}
$$

$$
= \begin{bmatrix} v(1,1) & v(1,2) & \ldots \\ v(2,1) & v(2,2) & \ldots \\ & \ldots \\ v(m,1) & v(m,2) & \ldots \end{bmatrix} * \begin{bmatrix} a1 & b1 & c1 & \ldots \\ a2 & b2 & c2 & \ldots \\ a3 & b3 & c3 & \ldots \\ & \ldots \end{bmatrix}
$$

$$
= D\sim * E\sim
$$

where we denote by E~ the matrix that has successive columns as the set of weights used to derive each of the principal components.

The first key point about the principal components is that the weights shown in E~ are chosen in such a way that each of the principal components has a correlation of 0 with each of the other principal components. In other words, if we calculate the correlation matrix for the set of principal components that would as before be transp(P~) * P~, then the resultant matrix would have numbers on the principal diagonal and 0s elsewhere.

The next key point is that the variances of the principal components will not all be equal to 1, as in the case of the original variables. The sum of their variances will add up to n as before, i.e., the total variance of the principal components will be the same as the total variance of the original variables. However, the weights can be chosen so that the first principal component, derived using weights of $a1$, $a2$ . . . has the largest variance out of the set of principal components, the second one has the next largest variance, and so on. (These

numbers representing the variances of the successive principal components, will appear on the principal diagonal of the correlation matrix of the principal components).

As a result, it would typically happen that a few of the principal components would capture most of the total variance of the original set of variables. It was the major goal of the technique that the variability in the original large set of variables could be captured by a smaller number of derived variables, making further analysis more convenient. For this reason, the method of principal components is sometimes described as a *data reduction technique*.

The crucial question is: how are these weights to be used for the "transformation matrix" E~ to be calculated to achieve the goal of having uncorrelated derived variables in which a few of them will capture most of the variability? The answer to this is connected with a property of square matrices: they have what are called *eigenvalues* and *eigenvectors* associated with them.

 # Eigenvalues and eigenvectors of matrix

Let's look at an example similar to the one we saw in the last appendix, where a row vector is multiplied by a square matrix:

$$[\ 2 \ \ 3 \ ] * \begin{bmatrix} 1 & 4 \\ 2 & -1 \end{bmatrix} = [\ 8 \ \ 5 \ ]$$

We saw that the effect of this multiplication is to change the direction in which the vector points. The direction pointed at by [2 3] is different from the direction of [8 5], as we can see from Fig. B-1. On the other hand, the direction of [2 3], [4 6], and [20 30] would all be the same, i.e., when both components of the vector are multiplied by the same number or scalar, the direction does not change, only the length of the vector or line connecting the point to 0,0 does. On the other hand, with the same matrix above consider the product:

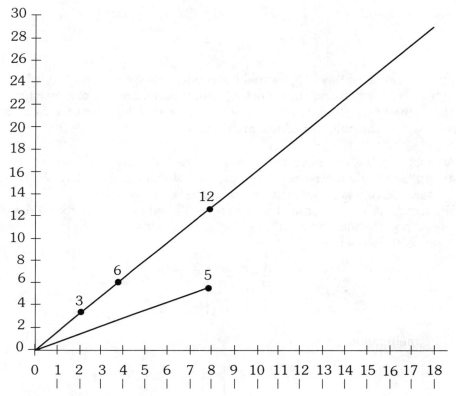

Directions: point 2,3 and 8,5.

$$[\ 1\ \ 1\ ] * \begin{bmatrix} 1 & 4 \\ 2 & -1 \end{bmatrix} = [\ 3\ \ 3\ ] = 3 * [\ 1\ \ 1\ ]$$

We see that for the vector [1 1], the multiplication does not change the direction. It only extends it by a factor of 3, i.e., scalar multiplies or changes the scale by 3. A vector whose direction is not changed by multiplying by a square matrix is called an eigenvector of the matrix, and the factor by which the vector is extended is called the associated eigenvalue. The matrix above has the eigenvector [1 1] with an eigenvalue of 3. It also has another eigenvector [1 – 2] with eigenvalue of –3.

$$[\ 1\ -2\ ] * \begin{bmatrix} 1 & 2 \\ 4 & -1 \end{bmatrix} = [\ -3\ 6\ ] = -3 * [\ 1\ -2\ ]$$

The relevance of this to principal components is as follows: the values to be used for deriving the principal components are the eigenvectors of C~, the correlation matrix of the original variables. The eigenvectors are used as the columns of the matrix E~.

A square matrix can have row eigenvectors, i.e., rows that when multiplied by the matrix on the right, do not change direction. What we saw above were row eigenvectors. There can be column eigenvectors, i.e., columns that when multiplied by the matrix on the left do not change direction. For the above matrix, a column eigenvector would be:

$$\begin{bmatrix} 2 \\ 1 \end{bmatrix}$$

since multiplying:

$$\begin{bmatrix} 1 & 4 \\ 2 & -1 \end{bmatrix} * \begin{bmatrix} 2 \\ 1 \end{bmatrix}$$

gives:

$$\begin{bmatrix} 6 \\ 3 \end{bmatrix} = 3 * \begin{bmatrix} 2 \\ 1 \end{bmatrix}$$

This means the associated eigenvalue is 3.

Clearly, any scalar multiple of an eigenvector would also be an eigenvector. In the example above, we saw that the direction of [1 1] is not changed by multiplication by the matrix, and so 3 * [1 1] = [3 3] = will also not change direction, nor will 5 * [1 1] = [5 5], and so on. It is therefore the practice to "normalize" the eigenvector. In the two-dimensional example above, we see that the length of the

vector [[1 1]], i.e., its distance from the point 0, 0, is given by Pythagoras theorem as:

length squared = 1 squared + 1 squared = 2

Normalization means to adjust the scale so that the length of the vector is 1, and this is done by dividing both components by sqrt(2). So the normalized eigenvector is [[1/sqrt(2) 1/sqrt(2)]]. Similarly, for the other eigenvector [[1 −2]], since the length of the vector is sqrt(1 + 4), the normalized eigenvector is [1/ sqrt(5) −2/sqrt(5)]. By an extension of the idea of length of a vector, the eigenvector of a 3-, 4- . . . dimensional eigenvector would also be normalized by dividing each of the components by the square root of the sum of squares of the components.

There have been a number of theoretical results developed over the years regarding eigenvectors: not all matrices would have eigenvectors, a square matrix of size n by n would have at most n eigenvectors, the column eigenvectors of a matrix would be the row eigenvectors of the transpose of the matrix, and so on. For our purposes here, what is important is that a correlation matrix would typically have its full complement of n eigenvectors, and these can be used to derive n principal components.

To illustrate this, let's say we have two variables, $V(*,1)$ $V(*,2)$, and their correlation matrix $C\tilde{}$ is:

$$\begin{bmatrix} 1 & .6 \\ .6 & 1 \end{bmatrix}$$

This matrix has two row eigenvectors associated with it, namely:

[1/sqrt(2) 1/sqrt(2)]

When the matrix is multiplied by this, we get the result:

1.6 * [1/sqrt(2) 1/sqrt(2)]

So the associate eigenvalue is 1.6. The second eigenvector is:

[1/sqrt(2) −1/sqrt(2)]

165

and when the matrix is multiplied by this we get:

$$0.4 * [\ 1/\ \text{sqrt}(2)\ -1\ /\text{sqrt}(2)\ \ ]$$

So, the theory of principal components tells us that if we form two principal components $pc(*,1)$ and $pc(*,2)$ from the original data, using the weights:

$$pc(*,1) = v(*,1) * 1/\text{sqrt}(2) + v(*,2) * 1/\text{sqrt}(2)$$

$$pc(*,2) = v(*,1) * 1/\text{sqrt}(2) - v(*,2) * 1/\text{sqrt}(2)$$

then the two derived variables $pc(*,1)$ and $pc(*,2)$ will be uncorrelated. What is more, since the two eigenvalues are 1.6 and 0.4, the first principal component $pc(*,1)$ will capture $1.6/(1.6 + 0.4)$, i.e., 80% of the total variance of the two variables.

The correlation matrix of the principal components, which is:

$$\text{transp}(P^{\sim}) * P^{\sim}$$

would come out as:

$$\begin{bmatrix} 1.6 & 0 \\ 0 & 0.4 \end{bmatrix}$$

This tells us that the two principal components are uncorrelated, and that the total variance of 2 of the two variables is now distributed as 1.6 for $pc(*,1)$ and 0.4 for $pc(*,2)$.

Neural networks as extractors of principal components

At the start of this appendix, we quoted Anderson's observation that principal components analysis is becoming increasingly important in the field of neural networks. Now that we have seen what principal components are, let's look at the connection between neural networks and principal components.

We have seen that, essentially, a neural network takes a list or input vector, which we might broadly regard as measurements of important features or characteristics. The training set supplied to a neural network constitutes in essence a series of observations of multivariate data. The values we see for the features are not necessarily independent: in other words, we have the same situation as in the multivariate data matrix considered above; there might be correlation between the values of the different features. If, therefore, the variability in the measurements can be captured by a smaller set of what we might call derived features (by analogy with the derived variables we saw above), we achieve considerable economy in representing the input information.

This highlights the importance of a landmark paper by Oja (see the Bibliography) in which he proved that a single neuron can be designed to do the following: with a simple modification of the basic learning rule for perceptrons that we considered earlier in the book, the neuron will adjust its weights in such a way that the set of weights it finally adopts is in fact the largest eigenvector of the correlation matrix of the input data. In the light of our previous discussion, what this means is that the output of the neuron is in fact the *first principal component*.

In other words, just as in standard statistical applications the large number of variables are reduced to a smaller number of principal components that capture most of the variability in the data, a neuron is in effect treating the first principal component as providing all the information necessary for classifying the set of features or variables that constitute the input. Hertz, Krogh, and Palmer (1991) point out that the general advantage of principal components analysis is that reduction of the number of original variables to a smaller set of derived variables makes it easier to search for clusters, and since searching for clusters is one of the key pattern recognition problems, the ability of neurons and neural networks to extract principal components is of central importance. As an example, they point out that by reducing the "dimensions" or number of variables to be considered, principal components can help in encoding data.

In *Neurocomputing 2* (see the Bibliography) there are papers that discuss in detail how neural networks perform principal component

analysis. One example shows how a neural network that performs image compression using the backpropagation algorithm is in effect doing so by converting the input data to its principal components and thereby achieving an eightfold compression. To go into the full details of the applications mentioned above would be beyond the scope of this appendix, but we hope the brief description is sufficient to indicate the connections between principal components and multivariate statistics. To conclude this discussion of the relationship between multivariate statistics and neural networks, we will look at another well-established statistical technique that has turned out to be very relevant to neural networks.

⇨ Linear discriminant analysis

The famous statistician Ronald Fisher developed a technique for analysis of multivariate data that is known as *linear discriminant analysis*. The problem addressed by this technique is the following: Suppose we have data about the values of a number of variables for a whole collection of units we are studying. Suppose further we know that these units belong to two or more distinctly different groups. Fisher originally considered the problem of separation into two groups, and others later extended the analysis to the problem of more than two groups.

Let's start by considering the principles involved in the case of two groups. As a specific example, we might have sets of measurements of various parts and aspects of the skulls recovered from archaeological sites. The different attributes such as width of skull, thickness of skull, and so on would be the different variables. Suppose further that we know that certain skulls in our sample are related to a certain tribe, i.e., they constitute a distinct group that is different from the set of skulls from another tribe, which constitutes a different group. Can we use the sample measurements we have as an indicator of group membership, so that we can say that, given a certain set of measurements, we can identify that skull as belonging to a particular group. We see this is again a classification or categorization problem.

Linear discriminant analysis is based on trying to form a weighted sum of the values of the variables for each of the units in the sample, to

calculate what we might call a *score* for each unit. The weighted sum is called a *linear discriminant function*. Whatever weights we might use, because of variability, each skull in the whole sample would have a different score, and even the skulls in each group would not have the same score. However, it seems plausible that the skulls in each group would have lesser variability among themselves.

The problem addressed by linear discriminant analysis is to find a set of weights so that the variability within each group is as small as possible, whereas the variability when we consider units between different groups is as large as possible. When the problem is extended to consider more than two groups, the aim is to calculate one discriminant function that will separate the first groups from the others, then the next to separate the second group from the rest, and so on.

Ideally, if we could find weights so that the scores for one group all lie between 5 and 10, for a second group between 12 and 16, for a third group between 20 and 25 and so on, then the score could be used to categorize or classify a skull of unknown provenance by looking at its score and seeing which "group range of scores" it falls in or is closest to. However, it might not always be possible to achieve such complete separation.

The aim of discriminant analysis is to find a way to calculate scores so as to minimize the proportion or percentage of cases that are misclassified, i.e., get a score that puts them in the wrong group. The theoretical solution developed by Fisher, and later extended by others, is closely related to the matrix of sums of squares and cross-products, and the correlation matrix, both of which we discussed above.

It was shown that the weights to be used for calculating scores should be as follows: A sum of squares and cross-products, matrix $T^\sim$, should be set for the collection of all the objects belonging to all the groups. It is designated T to indicate it is the "total" sum of squares. A matrix $W^\sim$ should be set up by finding the sum of squares and cross-products for each group separately, and then adding up these matrices. This matrix is designated $W^\sim$ to indicate that it is the sum of squares "within" the groups. The difference $B^\sim = T^\sim - W^\sim$ should be calculated.

It turns out that the eigenvectors of the matrix given by (W~) * B~ would be the weights that would give indices that would cause the smallest percentage of cases to be assigned to wrong groups. If the number of groups is g, and the number of variables is m, the number of such discriminant functions that can be calculated is the smaller of $g-1$ and m. With two groups, only one discriminant function would be used, with a cutoff point so that units with scores above the cutoff score would be assigned to one group, and those below the cutoff score would be assigned to the other group.

From this summary of the features of linear discriminant analysis, we can see the close relationship between the linear functions used by a perceptron and these linear discriminant functions. A difference in emphasis is that in the case of the perceptron the inability to handle linearly nonseparable groups was regarded as a serious fault, whereas in linear discriminant analysis, the focus was on reducing the percentage of cases wrongly classified. Nevertheless, the knowledge developed regarding discriminant analysis has again turned out to be useful in analysis of the classification or categorization performed by threshold units.

There are a number of other such relationships between multivariate statistical analysis and neural networks. A starting point for study of these would be the section on Statistics and Classification in the collection *Neurocomputing 2*, cited earlier.

Bibliography

Preface

Gallant, Stephen. 1993. *Neural network learning and expert systems*. Cambridge, MA: MIT Press.

Johnson, R. Colin and Chappel Brown. 1988. *Cognizers*. New York: John Wiley.

Introduction

Allman, William F. 1989. *Apprentices of wonder*. New York: Bantam Books.

Johnson, R. Colin, and Chappel Brown. 1988. *Cognizers*. New York: John Wiley.

Chapter 2

Lisboa, P.G.J., editor. 1992. *Neural networks: current applications*. New York: Chapman and Hall.

Maren, Alianna, Craig Harston, and Robert Pap. 1990. *Handbook of neural computing applications*. San Diego: Academic Press.

Rumelhart, David E. and James L. McClelland. 1986. *Parallel distributed processing, volume 1: foundations*. Cambridge, MA: MIT Press.

Sejnowski, T. J. and C.R. Rosenberg. 1988. "NETtalk" in Anderson and Rosenfeld, *Neurocomputing*. Cambridge, MA: MIT Press.

➡️ Chapter 3

Hopfield, J. J. 1982. Neural networks and physical systems with emergent collective properties. Proceedings of the National Academy of Sciences, 79, 2554–2558. This is the classic paper in which the Hopfield net was first described.

_____. 1984. Neurons with graded response have computational properties like those of two-state neurons. Proceedings of the National Academy of Sciences, 81, 3088–3092. Both of the papers are included in Anderson and Rosenfeld (1988).

➡️ Chapter 4

Ackley, D.H., G.E. Hinton and T.J. Sejnowski. 1985. A learning algorithm for Boltzmann machines. *Cognitive science* 9: 147–169.

Kirkpatrick, S., C.D. Gellat, Jr., and M.P. Vecchi. 1983. Optimization by simulated annealing: *Science* 220: 671–680. Both papers are included in Anderson and Rosenfeld (1986).

➡️ Chapter 5

Grossberg, Steven. 1988. *Neural networks and natural intelligence*. Cambridge, MA: MIT Press.

Carpenter, G. A. and S. Grossberg. 1988. The ART of adaptive pattern recognition by a self-organizing neural network. *Computer*, March 1988: 77–88.

Kohonen, Teuvo. The self-organizing map. Proceedings of the IEEE, September 1990.

⇨ Chapter 6

Anderson, James A., and Edward Rosenfeld. 1988. *Neurocomputing: foundations of research*. Cambridge, MA: MIT Press. In addition to other papers, this contains the classic papers by McCulloch and Pitts, Hebb, Widrow, Grossberg, Hopfield, Kohonen, and Sejnowski, the leading researchers whose works have been mentioned at various places in this book. This collection is a must for anyone interested in going further into the field of neural computing.

Anderson, James A., Andras Pellionisz, and Edward Rosenfeld. 1990. *Neurocomputing 2: directions for research*. Cambridge, MA: MIT Press. A follow-up volume and equally valuable.

Hebb, Donald. 1949. *The organization of behavior*. New York: John Wiley.

McClelland, James L., David E. Rumelhart and the PDP Research Group. 1986. *Parallel distributed processing, volume 2: psychological and biological models*. Cambridge, MA: MIT Press. These two volumes represent the work of the major researchers at the Institute for Cognitive Science at the University of California, San Diego. The books have the status of classics. They are not outdated because the fundamentals developed in this book still form the basis of current work.

Mehra, Pankaj and Benjamin W. Wah. 1992. *Artificial neural networks: concepts and theory*. Los Alamitos, CA: IEEE Press.

Rumelhart, David E., James L. McClelland, and the PDP Research Group. 1986. *Parallel distributed processing, volume 1: foundations*. Cambridge, MA: MIT Press.

Sanchez-Sinencio, Edgar, and Clifford Lau. 1992. *Artificial neural networks: paradigms, applications and hardware implementations*. Piscataway, NJ: IEEE Press. The two books by IEEE Press are collections of articles from a variety of publications. The IEEE Press has done a valuable job in publishing these collections that provide information on practically all aspects of neural computing.

⇨ Appendix B

Oja, E. 1982. A simplified neuron model as a principal component analyser. *Journal of mathematical biology* 15: 267-273.

Anderson, James A., Andras Pellionisz, and Edward Rosenfeld, editors. 1990. *Neurocomputing 2: directions for research.* Cambridge, MA: MIT Press.

Index

About the authors

Dr. Ramachandran Bharath is a professor of Computer Information Systems at Northern Michigan University in Marquette, Michigan. He is also the author of three other books (two on the subject of the computer language PROLOG for TAB/McGraw-Hill and one on graph theory for Ellis Horwood). Dr. James Drosen, who is a colleague of Dr. Bharath's, wrote the programs for the book and disk.

Other Bestsellers of Related Interest

Genesis Redux: Experiments Creating Artificial Life
Artificial life simulation for BASIC, C, and Pascal programmers.
Interactive programs on disk allow programmers to create complex,
dynamic organisms on their PCs. Makes cutting-edge research into
biotechnology, neural networks, artificial intelligence, robotics,
ecosystems, and cellular biology accessible. 240 Pages.
0-8306-4503-9 $29.95 Paper

Creating Artificial Life: Computer Modeling Experiments
Using computers to simulate complex, dynamic life forms—a project
book for BASIC, C, and Pascal programmers and advanced computer
hobbyists. Takes a provocative look at the future of artificial life and
its implications for 21st century society. Disk included. 256 Pages.
0-8306-4150-5 $29.95 Paper

Virtual Reality: Through the New Looking Glass
An illuminating inside look at the past, present, and future of
computer-generated artificial worlds—an introduction for general
readers. Includes extensive coverage of new research into affordable
VR applications for personal computers. 256 Pages.
0-8306-4064-9 $22.95 Paper
0-8306-4065-7 $32.95 Hard

Artificial Intelligence, 2nd Edition
An indispensable reference for computer scientists, engineers, and
psychologists. Includes new research findings and expanding
coverage of knowledge representation, reasoning, logic
programming, and other topics. 640 Pages.
0-07-052263-4 $38.95 Paper

How to Order

☎ **Call 1-800-822-8158**
24 hours a day,
7 days a week
in U.S. and Canada

✉ **Mail this coupon to:**
McGraw-Hill, Inc.
Blue Ridge Summit, PA
17294-0840

📠 **Fax your order to:**
717-794-5291

💻 **EMAIL**
70007.1531@COMPUSERVE.COM
COMPUSERVE: GO MH

Thank you for your order!

Shipping and Handling Charges

Order Amount	Within U.S.	Outside U.S.
Less than $15	$3.45	$5.25
$15.00 - $24.99	$3.95	$5.95
$25.00 - $49.99	$4.95	$6.95
$50.00 - and up	$5.95	$7.95

EASY ORDER FORM—
SATISFACTION GUARANTEED

Ship to:

Name _____

Address _____

City/State/Zip _____

Daytime Telephone No. _____

ITEM NO.	QUANTITY	AMT.

Method of Payment:

☐ Check or money order enclosed (payable to McGraw-Hill)

☐   ☐ *VISA*

☐ MasterCard ☐

Shipping & Handling charge from chart below	
Subtotal	
Please add applicable state & local sales tax	
TOTAL	

Account No. ☐☐☐☐☐☐☐☐☐☐☐☐☐☐

Signature _____ Exp. Date _____
Order invalid without signature

**In a hurry? Call 1-800-822-8158 anytime,
day or night, or visit your local bookstore.**

Code = BC44ZNA

DISK WARRANTY

This software is protected by both United States copyright law and international copyright treaty provision. You must treat this software just like a book, except that you may copy it into a computer in order to be used and you may make archival copies of the software for the sole purpose of backing up our software and protecting your investment from loss.

By saying "just like a book," McGraw-Hill means, for example, that this software may be used by any number of people and may be freely moved from one computer location to another, so long as there is no possibility of its being used at one location or on one computer while it also is being used at another. Just as a book cannot be read by two different people in two different places at the same time, neither can the software be used by two different people in two different places at the same time (unless, of course, McGraw-Hill's copyright is being violated).

LIMITED WARRANTY

Windcrest/McGraw-Hill takes great care to provide you with top-quality software, thoroughly checked to prevent virus infections. McGraw-Hill warrants the physical diskette(s) contained herein to be free of defects in materials and workmanship for a period of sixty days from the purchase date. If McGraw-Hill receives written notification within the warranty period of defects in materials or workmanship, and such notification is determined by McGraw-Hill to be correct, McGraw-Hill will replace the defective diskette(s). Send requests to:

> Customer Service
> Windcrest/McGraw-Hill
> 13311 Monterey Lane
> Blue Ridge Summit, PA 17294-0850

The entire and exclusive liability and remedy for breach of this Limited Warranty shall be limited to replacement of defective diskette(s) and shall not include or extend to any claim for or right to cover any other damages, including but not limited to, loss of profit, data, or use of the software, or special, incidental, or consequential damages or other similar claims, even if McGraw-Hill has been specifically advised of the possibility of such damages. In no event will McGraw-Hill's liability for any damages to you or any other person ever exceed the lower of suggested list price or actual price paid for the license to use the software, regardless of any form of the claim.

McGRAW-HILL, INC. SPECIFICALLY DISCLAIMS ALL OTHER WARRANTIES, EXPRESS OR IMPLIED, INCLUDING, BUT NOT LIMITED TO, ANY IMPLIED WARRANTY OF MERCHANTABILITY OR FITNESS FOR A PARTICULAR PURPOSE.

Specifically, McGraw-Hill makes no representation or warranty that the software is fit for any particular purpose and any implied warranty of merchantability is limited to the sixty-day duration of the Limited Warranty covering the physical diskette(s) only (and not the software) and is otherwise expressly and specifically disclaimed.

This limited warranty gives you specific legal rights; you may have others which may vary from state to state. Some states do not allow the exclusion of incidental or consequential damages, or the limitation on how long an implied warranty lasts, so some of the above may not apply to you.

IMPORTANT

Opening this package constitutes acceptance of the Disk Warranty terms and renders this entire book-disk package unreturnable except for replacement in kind due to material defect.

⇨ What's on the disk

BACKPROP.EXE
BACKPROP.C
BOLTZ.EXE
BOLTZ.C
HOPONE.EXE
HOPONE.C
HOPTWO.EXE
HOPTWO.C
HOPTWO-2.C
HOPTWO-2.EXE
KOHONEN.EXE
KOHONEN.C
LEARNIT.C
LEARNIT.EXE
MATRIX.C
MATRIX.EXE
MCPITTS.EXE
MCPITTS.C
READ_ME.TXT
SIGMOID.EXE
SIGMOID.C
SIGRESP.EXE
SIGRESP.C
SUMSQ.EXE
SUMSQ.C